Wizard of the dri[...]
follower of his l[...]
resemblance to At[...]
coincidental). His Les Bence character first
appeared in his own fanzine and was snapped up
for a seven-figure transfer by leading footie mag
When Saturday Comes.

Life at the Tip

Les Bence on the Game

Merv Grist

First published in Great Britain in 1993 by
Virgin Books
an imprint of Virgin Publishing Ltd
332 Ladbroke Grove
London W10 5AH

Copyright © Merv Grist 1993

The moral right of the author has been asserted

This book is sold subject to the condition that it shall not,
by way of trade or otherwise, be lent, resold, hired out or
otherwise circulated without the publisher's prior written
consent in any form of binding or cover other than that in
which it is published and without a similar condition
including this condition being imposed upon the subsequent
purchaser.

A catalogue record for this book is available from the British
Library

ISBN 0 86369 613 9

Illustrations by Phil Healey

Phototypeset by Intype, London
Printed and bound by
Cox & Wyman, Reading, Berks

ATHLETICO WHADDON FOOTBALL CLUB

FOUNDED 1911

FORMER NAMES Blazers Sleepibye Beds Sports and Welfare; Mitchley and Whaddon Athletic; Whaddon and Mitchley Athletic; Whaddon Athletic

CHAIRMAN Mr Kenneth Mentle OBE

MANAGER Mr Leslie Bence RAC

GROUND The Tip, Tip Lane (unclassified road), Mitchley Road

CAPACITY 750 (paying) 2,000 (non-paying)

RECORD ATTENDANCE 2,200 Mr Pastry and The Sooty Show (1963)

RECORD ATTENDANCE (ALLEGED) 200,000 v. Mitchley Borough (every year before the war)

RECORD WIN 5–0 v. Whaddon Methodist Sunday School XI (1947)

RECORD DEFEAT 13–1 v. Hexley Utd (1949); Felton (1957, 1973, 1989); Wendle Colliery Spartans (1951); Ogley (1948); Northtown FC (1977, 1987); Galvanised Steel Marwick (1966); Dagenham Girl Pipers XI (1971)

MOST GOALS IN A SEASON 672 (including training sessions)

MOST LEAGUE GOALS 31 (season 71/72)
MOST GOALS AGAINST approx. 301 (season 71/72; 75/76; 87/88; 88/89)
MOST CAPPED PLAYER none
PLAYER WITH MOST CAPPED TEETH Len Furlow (Whaddon 1968–70)
PLAYERS WITH LEAGUE/INTERNATIONAL EXPERIENCE Mike Channon (signing imminent)
LEAGUE AND CUP HONOURS see below

ATHLETICO WHADDON SUPPORTERS' CLUB NEWSLETTER

MANAGER'S WELCOME

BOTTOM OF DIVISION TWO (How they finished last season)

	P	W	D	L	F	A	PTS
Lake Town	34	10	10	14	83	56	40
Corwick Rgers	34	10	4	20	42	64	34
A. WHADDON	34	3	3	28	24	103	12

Good grief, no sooner has the final whistle blown than we here at Athletico Whaddon are gearing ourselves up ready for the hurly-burly of next season's campaign.

Our new home will be the Multivite Vegeburger/Singletons Valve Replacement League Division Three where the standard of football is remarkably high. Not, perhaps, of the calibre we experienced last season in Division Two, and admittedly falling far short of that which graced 'The Tip' during our brief spell in Division One. However, players excel and quality rises when one's team is being cheered on by four or five thousand enthusiastic fans and even the hundred plus that turn up here every week can lift a team, so, please, continue your support in the forthcoming season.

Relegation, it must be said, came hard, but of course was not a new experience here at Athletico Whaddon. After all, it was only a season ago that we were last relegated, but the spirit within the club is such that we can bounce right back,

3

of that I am sure. Personally, I take some comfort in knowing that I in no way contributed to our exit from Division Two. When I took over, the 'Whads' were already twenty points adrift from the rest of football and while not seeing myself beyond blame entirely, my denial of any involvement in our downfall does not mean my commitment is any less than 110 per cent. I would gladly have accepted the post of manager even if I had not won it in the club raffle.

Dedication is also the byword of our chairman, Mr Ken Mentle, and once again he has no hesitation in offering me a substantial amount of promises for next season. Ken's undying devotion to this club should be applauded by players, directors and supporters alike. For, even in these difficult times, he still holds dear the thought of League football arriving at 'The Tip'. As he said to me after relegation was confirmed last season, 'League football is still only fifteen divisions away, Les.'

Athletico Whaddon 1992–1993

MULTIVITE VEGEBURGER/ SINGLETONS VALVE REPLACEMENT LEAGUE DIVISION THREE FIXTURES 1992/1993

DATE	OPPONENT	VENUE
5 Sept.	CHAMDEN CITY RESERVES	A.
12 Sept.	SCRIMLEY ARSENAL	H.
16 Sept.	HELLINGBOROUGH	A.
19 Sept.	FRAMPTON ROVERS	A.
26 Sept.	BOTHAM WANDERERS	H.
29 Sept.	SIDCOMBE	A.
3 Oct.	SPORTING HYDRA CHEMICALS	A.
6 Oct.	GOSLING CELTIC	H.
10 Oct.	CLANSFORD UNITED	A.
17 Oct.	NORTHTOWN	A.
7 Nov.	REDLAND PARK AVENUE	H.
14 Nov.	BOTHAM WANDERERS	A.
21 Nov.	FELTON	H.
5 Dec.	TWITCHIT ALBION	A.
19 Dec.	DORNING TOWN	H.
26 Dec.	LEECH TOWN	A.
16 Jan.	SIDCOMBE	H.
26 Jan.	SCRIMLEY ARSENAL	A.
30 Jan.	CHAMDEN CITY RESERVES	H.
6 Feb.	FRAMPTON ROVERS	H.
20 Feb.	SPORTING HYDRA CHEMICALS	H.
23 Feb.	ALBORNE	A.

27 Feb.	NORTHTOWN	H.
6 Mar.	CLANSFORD UNITED	H.
13 Mar.	TWITCHIT ALBION	H.
20 Mar.	DORNING TOWN	A.
23 Mar.	FELTON	A.
3 Apr.	ALBORNE	H.
13 Apr.	REDLAND PARK AVENUE	A.
17 Apr.	LEECH TOWN	H.
24 Apr.	GOSLING CELTIC	A.
1 May	HELLINGBOROUGH	H.

LES IN CONFIDENCE

MONDAY, 7th SEPTEMBER
LABOUR DAY (CANADA)

Dear God, I must give up drink.

It was drink that got me into this mess. That and the club raffle. If I had kept my wits and remained coherent I would probably have realised the manager's job was third prize. If I had been sober I would never have bloody claimed it! Still, at least I put my bottle where my mouth is, not like those whingeing sods at 'The Tip'.

It dawned on me last season, as we took a first-minute lead over Carlton Town West Saxons, that perhaps it was Fate that plucked pink, 544, from the hat. At that moment of jubilation I realised that my own philosophy on life and that of football management go hand in foot. Surely it cannot be long before the Football League discovers what is festering in the Multivite Vegeburger/ Singletons Valve Replacement League sewer. Should the FA come calling I would take any managerial post offered, even Coventry City.

But what have I got? Athletico Whaddon. A bunch of boozed up neverbeens who would struggle to get a draw against half a box of Subbuteo. I might fool the fans, but the best I can hope for this season must be second from bottom and the third preliminary round of the FA Cup. OK, we kicked off with a win at Chamden, but they only had five men and most of those looked old enough to remember Bolton Wanderers on *Match of the Day*. As for my shower, only Marley looks like he might have talent, he seems capable of scoring goals with either his left or his right buttock.

7

WEDNESDAY, 9th SEPTEMBER

Two days to go before the first home game of the season. Programme notes and a bottle of Bells to get through.

Mentle has suggested I do a flattering team profile, but fiction was never my strong point. How the hell does he expect me to keep a straight pen? Look at Micky Deere, he's a complete waste of space. He's as short-sighted as a bat with its eyes shut, but with his goggles on he is a lousy attacker and without them a serious threat to our defence! Phil Meek is no improvement. God knows what Pybus saw in him, because if you could buy skill Meek would be bankrupt and still a crap player. Likewise his other 'great' find, Colin Webley. Do me a favour, Webley couldn't even pass a mug of tea across the counter last season, let alone pass a ball.

Thankfully, that win backed up my insistence that we re-sign Trevor Proby. It had been tough going, but Proby was grateful enough to knock a century off the £500 I owe him. Ken Mentle argued that Trevor needed psychiatric treatment more than another chance in an Athletico shirt. Well, I am no medical man, but that is an understatement.

I must look out Chester's Junior Trustees Savings Account Book. Surely, if I beg nicely, he will lend his old dad four hundred quid.

MANAGER'S NOTES

P	W	D	L	F	A	PTS
1	1	0	0	2	1	3

Well, here we go into our first home game of the new season with a 100 per cent record so far in Division Three. Our surprise away win at Chamden City Reserves last Saturday means that Athletico Whaddon has its first unbeaten run in nineteen seasons. WELL DONE, LADS!

This was a thoroughly inspired performance by the team, for which I must take all the credit. It was unfortunate for spectators that Chamden were unable to raise a full side but this should not detract from our victory, although all praise to the five Chamden lads for holding our rampant attack to a slender 2–1.

The only sad note of the afternoon was the heart attack suffered by our chairman, Ken Mentle, just after the final whistle. I am pleased to report that Ken's attack was not major and that he is well on the way to recovery. I am sure we all wish him the best of luck. GET WELL SOON, SON.

*   *   *   *   *   *   *

Today sees the debut of a number of new and not so new summer signings. Royston Marley comes to us from Ross Chicken Ltd. The Jamaican-born centre-forward (37) spent much of last season at Spurs where he watched every home game.

Other new faces this season: Jason Pratt is a 15-year-old 'find' by club coach Reg Pybus. Jason hails from St Dodimeads Comprehensive School whose Under-14 side held us to a very creditable 0–0 draw two seasons ago in the County Knock-Out Shield. He is a talented lad who shows great respect for his elders and will play in any position I tell him to. Colin Webley (36) is another newcomer as far as playing is concerned, although many of you will know him as the chap who did sterling work in the tea hut last season. Colin, a born darts player, was so keen to play for the 'Whads' that he paid his own signing-on fee (£56), and has also agreed to wash the team strip every week. Colin will play at left back and is club captain for the season. We also welcome back a former club captain, Trevor 'Killer' Proby (52) after a four-year suspension. Trevor, experienced in attack and abuse to officials, will prove invaluable. Many supporters, I know, feel uneasy that Proby is returning and are dismayed that we have not seen the last of what the *Whaddon and Mitchley Argus* called 'The Headcase Half Back'.

Let me put forward the case for re-signing Proby. Despite a disciplinary record that reflects his competitive nature, Trevor has a lot of skill and in many ways is a credit to the side. Football is a hard game for hard men. There is no room for a player with kid gloves on his feet, no room for sentiment, only sediment out there on the park. When you are on rung 356 of soccer's hierarchical ladder you have to fight all the way. When Trevor Proby has the ball between his legs he is a very big cog in the 'Whads' wheel. Non-League football is not about offside traps and delicate passing skills, it is about clogging and war. Wars are won by tanks not soft tackles. Remember that.

The rest of this season's squad has a lot of old faces in it. Many of these stalwarts could, I am sure, play at a higher level of football and we are lucky that their devotion to the club and my management skills keep them here. Micky Deere (49), one of our longest serving players, has proved time and again how badly we need an experienced defender. This season Micky will be sporting some new lenses, over four inches thick, in his match-day bi-focals. Young goalie, John Slack (38), has recovered from a dislocated shoulder and broken nose he sustained during a pre-season tactical discussion with Trevor Proby and is eager to take up that vital position between the posts once again. At 53 most players would have only dusty memories of their days in combat, but Dave Doyle, the 'Cliff Richard of football', still turns out every season for his beloved Whaddon. It is only natural that his pace has slowed and perhaps that gazelle-like mind, which was such an influence on the young George Best, may have dulled, but if I had eleven Dave Doyles in my side then we would make the *Guinness Book Of Records* and cause referees and opponents utter confusion. Confused is a word I would use to describe Darren Twink's (24) dazzling ball skills. 'Twinky' is now in his second season with us after failing to make his mark in Sunday football. Here at Whaddon I have allowed his talent to blossom and I would not be surprised to see the League big boys sniffing after him before Christmas, and Darren to be a regular in Barnet reserves by the end of the season. Despite openly admitting to owning the entire recorded works of Chicory Tip, Terry Wade (44) does not let his eccentricities interfere with his on-field performance; despite his refusal to turn out on Eurovision Song Contest ay. Last season, remember, he headed three glorious goals before the FA banned his innovative platform football boots. Angus 'Jock' McDougall (56) is currently the only Polish player on Athletico's books. Ever since he was a young lad, 'Jock' has harboured ambitions of playing professional soccer. Unfortunately, he has never made the grade and after knocking on the door of inter-pub midweek leagues without success, has at last found his niche at Athletico where this season he will team up with YTS trainees Adie Smith and Phil Meek. Finally, Steve Gillery is with us again. Signed two seasons ago from Dunwick Pressed Steel Reserves where he was unable to sustain a second team place, he has found his perfect football niche here at Whaddon.

*　　　*　　　*　　　*　　　*　　　*　　　*

As no doubt the teams are ready to take the field, it only remains for me to extend a warm welcome to the directors, players and boisterous supporters of Scrimley Arsenal and wish you all an enjoyable afternoon.

SPOTLIGHT ON ATHLETICO
WHADDON 1911–1940

It was the formation of the Mid-Counties Combination League, now the Alaap Curry Mix Intermediate, that took Athletico Whaddon forerunners Blazers Sleepibye Beds Sports and Welfare FC from a works eleven to footballing representatives for the borough of Mitchley and Whaddon.

'The Beds' were formed in 1911 by local manufacturer, sportsman and historian, the eccentric P. W. Blazer. It was he who walked from Bristol to London via Glasgow and Edinburgh in papyrus sandals to prove his theory that all Roman roads turned right. Blazer offered his workforce a piece of waste ground behind the mattress shed for a pitch and it soon became affectionately known as the 'Football Ground'. Owing to an archaic local by-law, which forbade the wearing of shorts in an industrial building at weekends, the changing rooms were three miles away at the Duck and Forceps public house.

The bed magnate took charge of the team himself and could often be seen running the touchline in his pith helmet, armed with an old shotgun to encourage the lads. Leg wounds were common among players in those early days and contributed to the team's poor performances. Between 1912 and 1930 their most successful period was 1914–18 when all football was suspended because of the First World War.

By 1926, the stuffing had been knocked out of the mattress business and the factory closed. Mr Blazer also died that year and as a mark of respect and lack of interest the club folded, only to re-appear in 1931, widening their appeal by becoming Mitchley and Whaddon Athletic. However, after a lively inaugural meeting at the Duck and Forceps, punches were thrown, beer spilt and the club emerged as Whaddon and Mitchley Athletic. Then, just before the club's debut v. Cromley Royal Artillery (1931) Ltd, fighting broke out in the dressing room and the Mitchley contingent in the crowd were surprised to discover the team was five players short and called Whaddon Athletic. With five volunteers from the 400-plus crowd, a 12–1 defeat at the hands of the soldiers was not a bad start.

The following week, an application was made to the county Sunday League by the breakaway quintet and friends as the rival Mitchley Borough. Over the years a niggling rivalry has been much in evidence between the two clubs, although Whaddon have progressed to a much higher standard of football. Mitchley, on the other hand, have deservedly spent sixty-odd years rotting in the wastelands of Sunday soccer, their only consolation being that they have won all twenty-six encounters between the two clubs since 1932.

Local grocer, Fred Plumb, became the first Athletic manager in 1932 by winning the position in a raffle, thereby setting a tradition which has continued to this day. Fred, a man of immense charm and cunning, was the man who first suggested looking beyond the lounge bar of the Duck and Forceps for potential players. Up until then, the only qualifications needed to secure a place in the team were an abnormal capacity for Nettles Agricultural Sherry, a willingness to buy a round whenever invited, an abhorrence of physical exercise and a pair of knee-length shorts. It was Fred who signed and elected Duck and Forceps landlord Bill Dodd as club captain. Despite the fact that Bill was in his mid-fifties and had a chronic heart condition, which meant he could only play for a maximum of five minutes a match, it was a good move on Fred's part as the pub owned the cricket pitch at the rear and naturally, as captain, Bill felt obliged to hand it over to the club, and so 'The Tip' was born. By the end of the 32/33 season, the club was well placed to progress from friendlies to Junior

League soccer. The opportunity arose in the close season when the FA decided to form the Mid-Counties Combination.

Whaddon saw their acceptance into the Combination as the first tentative step towards professional League football, and work was undertaken over the next five years on building and improving basic facilities at 'The Tip'. We should perhaps remember that, before the advent of television, the five-day week and DIY superstores, crowds, even for the smallest clubs, often exceeded 3,000 and for an important derby match during the 1930s Whaddon could easily pull in 120,000 fans according to some of the club's more senior supporters.

The old cricket pavilion was demolished and then cobbled back together as a grandstand able to accommodate up to fifty spectators. Ex-GWR rolling stock was soldered together, the sides removed and transformed into the popular 'Bog Hole' where today long-time supporters huddle. On the field, however, progress proved slow and fourteenth (out of sixteen) during the 35/36 season was our most notable achievement. Bill Dodd's retirement saw Cyril Proby take over the captaincy and Plumb began the job of squad rebuilding. Some of the names he enlisted will no doubt bring back fond memories for older supporters – names like Bert Fudge, 'Shin Hack' Hodges and, of course, the (then) young Kenny Mentle.

Ken's skill as a player was evident from the start. Here was a footballer the like of which the Whaddon faithful had never witnessed before. Here was a player who had clean kit for every match, who actually trained at home and, more importantly, scored goals where it mattered – between the posts.

The following two seasons saw a steady improvement in team performance, consolidating their fourteenth position from the previous season and finishing a creditable ninth (out of ten) in 36/37.

Once again, the league structure was to change, and the formation of a semi-professional super-league of five divisions was announced. Heading the new Mid-Counties

16

South-West League (Northern Division) was to be a Premier Division to which all Combination clubs were invited to apply. The FA took a unique decision here, declaring that clubs would be elected alphabetically to the five divisions. Fred Plumb now pulled a masterstroke. On the day of application he convened an extraordinary board meeting and, within minutes, announced that Whaddon Athletic was now known as Athletico Whaddon, thus ensuring Premier rather than Fifth Division football.

As the 1938/39 season began, an off-the-field crisis occurred. The club cashbox containing £3 2s 8d, two Co-op milk tokens and a First World War medal went missing. It was later traced by police to the locker of club skipper Cyril Proby. With 92 other offences taken into consideration, including arson, blackmail, three sendings-off and a professional foul, Proby was sent down and dismissed by the club. Ironically, almost fifty years later, his son Trevor, also a club captain, secured an even longer stretch at Her Majesty's pleasure.

Under the new captaincy of Ken Mentle, the club decided not to go all out for the title but simply to consolidate their Premier Division status. The idea was certainly sensible as the club gained valuable experience, finished bottom, and were relegated to Division One.

However, if Athletico had hopes of a brief stay away from the Premier they were to be disappointed. By 1940 Nazi Germany, the Wimbledon of world politics, had started up a completely different ball game.

LES IN CONFIDENCE

SATURDAY, 26th SEPTEMBER

I have just returned from today's match dazed and confused. How the hell my pack of jokers has managed two wins out of two is a complete mystery. I told them in the club bar that it was all down to my carefully structured pre-season training programme, but after last season's relegation I haven't been near the ground since April! Actually, I am trying a new strategy. Before both last week's Chamden game and this afternoon's, I fell to my knees and uttered the following words, 'Oh God, please, please, please let us win today. I promise on my old mother's teeth that I will never drink or take Bobby Charlton's name in vain again. Thank you, God, thank you.' Well, it seems to work.

I thought the victory over Chamden would put an end to the ridicule and abuse the Whaddon 'rotweillers' have subjected me to, but no chance. Today's game I thought would be a good opportunity to rub the buggers' noses in it. I got to the ground early and strung up a 'Well done Les' banner over the turnstile, but in less than ten minutes Micky Deere had wiped his nose on one end and cleaned last week's mud off his boots with the other. Still, I was determined to cash in on my success and maintain a high profile at the ground. I greeted fans on their arrival with a shake of the hand and an offer to autograph their match programmes at a reasonable £1.50 a time. Of course, I knew my success would cause resentment. I have been a manager long enough to know the fans only look on me as a punch bag, constantly on the end of the verbal one-two. My new fedora and Hamlet cigar accessories, more fitting to a winning manager than my old tartan pom-pom cap and ounce of Old Holborn, made me unrecognisable to most of the supporters and the nearest I received to a compliment came from a director who suggested I 'stick a faggot up my backside and clear off'. Well, the way things are going this season I could well be clearing off. I have it on good authority from a cousin in Stockport, who has a drinking buddy who knows the car park attendant at Altrincham, that my name has already been linked with a managerial post at both Rotherham and Manchester United. Let me tell you, when those dubbin-lickers at Whaddon go on their knees and beg me to bring my United first team squad to 'The Tip' to put a few quid in their ailing coffers, I shall take great delight in treading on Ken Mentle's fingers, provided he survives last week's heart attack, and raising two toes in a defiant 'get lost' gesture.

I am the first person to admit that success is not that frequent at Athletico and on those rare occasions when it comes we are always left with a nasty aftertaste to spoil it. That aftertaste is Trevor Proby. The Lord knows I did my best. As soon as I heard that Mr Hudd would be linesman today I begged the League to appoint a different official. It was Hudd, five seasons ago, who waved his flag furiously at referee Hobbs when, unsighted, he failed to spot Proby forcing his shinpad down the throat of Mossborough Sandinista's Keith Driscoll until alerted by the enthusiastic linesman.

I have known Trevor for many years and he is a mass of seething hate before breakfast most days, so I could smell the revenge in him even above 'Jock' McDougall's armpits before we left the changing room this afternoon. It came as no surprise when he was sent off for a vicious headbutt to the hapless Hudd.

After the match Trevor and I had a heated argument

over what will, undoubtedly, be another suspension. I got nowhere, of course, because in an argument Trevor can be very persuasive.

REMEMBER: HAVE A FURTHER X-RAY ON THE MIDDLE FINGERS OF MY LEFT HAND ON TUESDAY.

ATHLETICO WHADDON

M/SV. DIVISION 3.

TODAY · V · BOTHAM WANDERERS

£1

* OFFICIAL PROGRAMME *

	P	W	D	L	PTS
GOSLING CELTIC	4	3	1	0	10
ATH. WHADDON	4	3	1	0	10
NORTHTOWN	4	3	0	1	9
ALBORNE	4	3	0	1	9
CLANSFORD UTD	4	2	2	0	8
REDLAND PARK AVENUE	4	2	1	1	7
SCRIMLEY ARSENAL	4	2	0	2	6
FELTON	4	2	0	2	6
DORNING TOWN	4	1	2	1	5
FRAMPTON ROVERS	4	1	2	1	5
HELLINGBOROUGH	4	1	1	2	4
LEECH TOWN	4	1	1	2	4
CHAMDEN CITY RESERVES	4	0	2	2	2
SIDCOMBE	4	0	2	2	2
SPORTING HYDRA CHEMICALS	4	0	2	2	2
TWITCHIT ALBION	4	0	2	2	2
BOTHAM WDRS	4	0	0	4	0

MANAGER'S NOTES

26th September '92
WE DO NOT REFUND ENTRANCE MONEY.

May I take this opportunity to say how sickened I was by the small group of supporters hounding the ticket kiosk for their money back, after Monday night's County Shield match against Whaddon YMCA.

Such is the standard of junior sides in this competition that the game appeared to be no more than a formality for us, so our 4–1 defeat came as a complete surprise. What supporters seem to overlook is that football is a game of two sides – one side has to lose otherwise it is a draw. Whaddon YMCA were a completely unknown quantity. At kick-off their team, like the match programme, was a blank sheet. After witnessing their performance I am not sure those supporters who thought they spotted four or five Danish internationals in the side (probably on a hiking tour of Britain), were mistaken. If this was indeed the case, then I think we played exceptionally well.

I am not offering excuses, but up against such class it was unfortunate that we could not field a side at full strength. Royston Marley's decision to work a permanent nightshift means he is now unavailable for anything but a three o'clock kick-off. We were also without that rock in defence, Trevor Proby. 'Killer', as you probably know, is currently under suspension following the harmless headbutting of a linesman during the Scrimley Arsenal game, and this has left a big hole in Mr Hudd's forehead, not to mention our defence.

Anyway, defeat in the County Shield may be for the best because, let's not be hasty, but after just four games we look like having Division Three wrapped up. You may recall we overcame a spirited Chamden side in the opening fixture, then handed out a 1–0 demolition to Scrimley Arsenal (Marley 58 mins), slaughtered Hellingborough on their own ground 2–1 (three own goals by 'Borough's one-eyed left back, Hazlett), then massacred Frampton Rovers in last Saturday's impressive 1–1 draw. Has there even been a better start to the season? How about a standing ovation for the team when they take the field this afternoon?

COMEONYOUWHADS!

*   *   *   *   *   *   *

One man who, if possible, would be leading the cheering today is, of course, our chairman, Mr Ken Mentle. Unfortunately Ken's recovery has suffered a setback after seeing us still in the title race with only fourteen-sixteenths of the season remaining. In his absence, fellow director Mr Pahdra Singh, well known proprietor of the 8-Day Superette and Pahdra's Palace take-away, has taken over the day-to-day business of chairman. Mr Singh is young, enthusiastic and full of far-reaching ideas for this club. Already he has called an extra-ordinary meeting of directors and supporters to discuss his radical new proposals.

*   *   *   *   *   *   *

Our visitors today, Botham Wanderers, are without a win so far this season and may possibly face liquidation before its end. Like our own, Botham's finances are a little under the weather. However, Wanderers are true amateurs on the field and will no doubt battle until they give up, so let's hope Athletico can keep up the good work and send them home with three lost points and the Samaritans' telephone number.

*   *   *   *   *   *   *

Today's match ball has been sponsored by the Black Sheep Wool Shop, Mitchley High Street. It will be a new experience for both Wanderers and ourselves to play with a knitted football.

YOUR LINE TO LES

Dear Les,

During our last home match of last season, I thought the team played exceedingly well all things considered. There was a lot of passing, running about and kicking which I found encouraging for this season.

However, my enjoyment in witnessing this rejuvenated Athletico is spoilt by the fact that Terry Wade has so far persisted in wearing white shorts whilst the rest of his team mates wear the customary black. Not only do I find this displeasing on the eye but I feel it contributed significantly to our eventual relegation.

Were the odd shorts some sort of tactical move, Les?

Yours, J.H.

J.H.

How observant of you to spot that Terry Wade's shorts were a different colour and to suspect this was a tactical ploy. Of course it was.

If you cast your mind back to the 1966 World Cup, you may recall that Pak Doo Ik, the North Korean forward, also wore odd shorts and he went on to score the winner against Italy, so I thought it was worth a try.

Yours in charge,
Les Bence

Dear Mr Bence,

I have been a supporter of this club since before the war, so I know what I am talking about.

Honestly, Les, this team is the biggest load of rubbish we

have had here since I've been a supporter and I started before the war, so I know what I am talking about.

> No offence, Les,
> Mr G.B.
> (Whaddon Light Infantry, retired)

G.B.

How nice to receive a letter so full of constructive criticism. Such an in-depth analysis of last season's loss of form obviously gives me food for thought and deserves a similarly constructive reply. Thank you for writing.

> Les Bence

NOTE TO PRINTERS – PLEASE MAKE SURE THE ONE BELOW IS REMOVED! ! – LB

Dear Les,

The photographs you asked for have arrived from Amsterdam and are awaiting collection. I shall be at the back of the newsagents after midnight on Sunday. If you do not arrive I will leave the pics in the dustbin.

These are pretty hot stuff so it is £80 I am afraid. Leave the money in the third bottle of embrocation from the left.

> Ted

Dear Ted,

Please do not send my personal mail addressed to the football club.

SPOTLIGHT ON ATHLETICO WHADDON 1940–1950

When war came, hostilities ended and the League disbanded for the duration.

This proved to be a frustrating time for the 'Whads', as, although fellow League clubs were losing players left, right and centre-half to the war effort, Athletico had no one fit to fight. Even dynamic centre-forward Kenny Mentle was found to be flat-footed and short-sighted. Ironically, during the war years, the pitch was in better condition than it had ever been, as it was given over to the growing of carrots and potatoes.

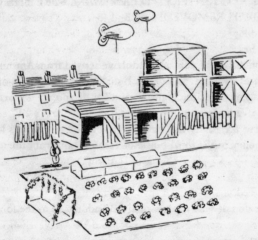

The Tip during wartime, by kind permission of Mrs Ethel Plumb

In 1943, practically the entire team relegated during 39/40 got back together during 'Buy a Spitfire' week to play a fund-raising match against a local Women's Land Army XI.

The match revealed the Athletico lads had lost none of their flair and inadequacies for the game as they narrowly went down to a 7–2 defeat. At the end of 1944 the goal posts once again replaced bean poles and 'The Tip' staged its own international fixture when a combined German and Italian team from the nearby POW camp took on the 'Whads', who for this match played under the name of England. They were awarded international caps, beautifully knitted by Mrs Ethel Plumb and presented by Lord Mitchley before the kick-off. The match was a hard-fought contest and after much cheating on their part, the prisoners ran out 3–0 victors with a doubtful hat-trick by Rudolph Hess. Justice was rightly done, however, when they lost the war and were again humiliated at Wembley in 1966.

Owing to a bizarre mix-up between a Japanese morse operator in the South China Sea, and new early closing times at Whaddon Post Office, when football finally got back to normal in 1946, Athletico, now fielding eleven internationals, found themselves in the Mid-Counties Combination instead of the higher Mid-Counties South-West League (Northern Division).

This was not the only blow to the club. The 46/47 season saw the forced retirement of Ken Mentle after he was struck on the knee by a lettuce thrown from a nearby allotment. On giving up as a player, Ken was a natural choice for chairman and, as he did at the end of every subsequent season, promised sweeping changes and League football by 1992.

First to go was manager Fred Plumb. By 1947, Fred was a broken man addicted to alcohol and the treble chance. His downfall was brought about by a lengthy court case in which he was wrongly accused of harbouring three war criminals (former POWs) in the Whaddon forward line.

The new man in charge was former goalkeeper, Walter 'Wally' Smott. Wally was awarded the job for his bravery in receiving extensive brain surgery after years of concussing himself on the crossbar. However, despite brain cells having been grafted from his backside, Walter staved off relegation and 1950 was heralded, by players and supporters alike, as the dawning of a new decade.

LES IN CONFIDENCE

WEDNESDAY, 23rd SEPTEMBER

It is nearly two weeks since I last touched a drink and we are still undefeated in the League. The bottle was in my hand, though, after that YMCA debacle. When that final whistle went I just wanted to throw up in the sponge bag. They were nothing more than a lousy bunch of down and outs, students (same thing in my book), and back-packing evangelists with acne. Most of them had to be introduced to one another by the referee yet they still stuffed four past us.

Luckily, my after-match tantrum in the dressing room certainly shook up my rabble and got a good performance against Frampton. They might be a conglomerate of poseurs, ex-Leaguers and Mike Channon wannabees, but they are also the best club in the division. I have cried off training tonight. My breathing is still suffering difficulties thanks to the custard slice that bastard Proby thrust up my nostrils. I persuaded Chester to cash in his Trustees account after agreeing to pay five quid for the taxi to take him to the bank. He had £2.10 in his account. Trevor was not happy.

Old mother Mentle phoned earlier to say hubbie Ken has calculated our current league position and suffered a relapse. This time it looks serious and if he is forced to resign then my own position could be in jeopardy. Ken Mentle is my only support on the board. This is hardly surprising I suppose as he recognised my managerial potential from the start. On my first day in the job he took me into the director's Portakabin, put his arm around me and, showing me the empty trophy case,

33

said 'Your job, Les, is to fill that cabinet before I die.'
No chance, Ken.

Just a couple of months out for Mentle would be
enough for Pahdra Singh to cause havoc. It is an open
secret that he and Reg Pybus are bosom pals. How else
could Pybus afford to dine out at Pahdra's take-away
and gain exclusive use of his portable telephone on
Saturday afternoons to call the Multivite Vegeburger/
Singletons Valve hotline? I have also noticed their peculiar handshake and the strange, but identical, way in
which they fold their match programmes 42 times. It
seems pretty obvious they both attend the same origami
evening class.

ATHLETICO · WHADDON

M/SV. DIVISION 3

TODAY · V · GOSLING CELTIC

£1

✱ OFFICIAL PROGRAMME ✱

	P	W	D	L	PTS
GOSLING CELTIC	8	5	2	1	17
REDLAND PARK AVENUE	8	4	3	1	15
CLANSFORD UTD	8	4	3	1	15
FRAMPTON ROVERS	8	4	2	2	14
HELLINGBOROUGH	8	4	1	3	13
ALBORNE	8	4	1	3	13
ATH. WHADDON	8	4	1	3	13
NORTHTOWN	8	3	3	2	12
FELTON	8	4	0	4	12
SCRIMLEY ARSENAL	8	3	2	3	11
SPORTING HYDRA CHEMICALS	8	2	3	3	9
TWITCHIT ALBION	8	2	3	3	9
DORNING TOWN	8	1	4	3	7
LEECH TOWN	8	1	4	3	7
CHAMDEN CITY RESERVES	8	1	3	4	6
SIDCOMBE	8	1	3	4	6
BOTHAM WDRS	8	1	1	6	4

MANAGER'S NOTES

6th October '92

I have received a number of dog faeces through my letterbox this week from some of our more fanatical 'supporters' after our defeats against Botham and at Sidcombe last Tuesday evening. Well, I hope they eat their post after our 1–0 thrashing of Sporting Hydra Chemicals.

Rarely have I seen the 'Whads' play with such composure, flair and skill. Stuffing the 'Hydracals' will be one of my most cherished memories when I look back on my spell as manager of Athletico Whaddon. As for those defeats at the hands of Botham and Sidcombe I would rate both, in footballing terms, as nightmares. To allow Botham Wanderers, who at the time were without a win, to take a four-goal lead was asking for trouble. I had expected them at that stage to do the decent thing and wait for us to catch up but, smelling their first blood of the season, they continued in much the same fashion and eventually ran out 7–0 victors.

I can offer little in the way of explanation for our disappointing display, although the failure of goalkeeper John Slack to turn up severely crippled the team. I was forced to put Micky Deere between the posts and the referee's insistence that he remove his bi-focals meant he was two fathoms below useless. Obviously, such a run of bad luck, after the fabulous start to the season, jolted the lads and their performance at Sidcombe must have warmed the hearts of those seven supporters who travelled to the game. There can be no doubt that we benefited from having 'Slacky' back in goal. I felt he had a particularly fine game and brought off some devastating rugby tackles on the Sidcombe forwards. It was, however, unfortunate that he could not save the resultant penalties which gave Sidcombe an undeserved 3–0 win.

*   *   *   *   *   *   *

Today we take on the League leaders, Gosling Celtic, and will be out to prove our Top Ten position is no fluke. Our team will be as near full strength as possible, although once again injuries are beginning to dog us. Out today are Micky Deere (headache), Royston Marley (badly pecked knees) and Steve Gillery (shopping). With no money to invest in new players and a squad of only thirteen, team selection is a constant problem. Today is a good case in point as both myself (21) and coach Reg Pybus (48–66?) may be called upon to play, along with a guest supporter should one step forward.

*   *   *   *   *   *   *

The need for cash has never been more urgent. Only this week, our shower and changing room have been declared a disaster area by the council. This follows the near drowning of a Public Health official. After ninety bruising minutes in the mire that is 'The Tip', the last thing we or our opponents will want on a fridge-like February Saturday, is a three-mile walk to the local Duck and Forceps' washroom, caked in mud and soggy shorts smelling as evil as a gypsy's knickers. Not only are we desperate to acquire funds for new dressing room facilities but an unfortunate accident with the club van, by person(s) unknown, has removed the tea hut. After many years in its free-standing position it now finds itself neatly stacked against the side of the grandstand. The club needs an immediate cash injection of £8,000. I am pleased to announce, therefore, that acting chairman, Mr Pahdra Singh, has secured a sponsorship deal with local funeral directors, Lonsdale and Pugh. Through this lucrative arrangement the club will receive £500 over the next ten years and the donation of a new team strip, on show for the first time today. Purple satin shorts,

38

royal blue shirts and black socks will give us an impressive appearance and put the fear of death in opponents. In honour of our new partnership with Messrs Lonsdale and Pugh, the team will, from today, be adopting a new nickname, THE STIFFS.

In Deepest Sympathy

LONSDALE
& PUGH

FUNERAL DIRECTORS

are pleased to
associate with
ATHLETICO
WHADDON

Bouquets and Wreaths to order

SPOTLIGHT ON ATHLETICO
WHADDON 1951–1969

Tom Finney, Stanley Matthews, Nat Lofthouse, Harry Lauder. How is that for a line up?

Stan Reynolds, Harry Little, Carl Einstien and Fred Grummidge may not have the same ring about them but between 1950 and 1960 these were the names on the footballing tongues of Whaddon.

Carl Einstien – the ex-POW who sold the 'Whaddon and Mitchley Sporting Mauve' outside 'The Tip' as you left the match.

Harry Little – the turnstile operator who would let you in for a penny or five Capstan Full Strength.

Fred Grummidge – the lovable old groundsman who grew dahlias along the touchline, and upon his death had his still red-hot ashes scattered across 'The Tip' and in so doing burnt down the dressing room.

Finally, the unforgettable Stan Reynolds, a player who so loved scoring goals that he would attempt to do so in whichever net was nearest. A dull 0–0 defence-dominated, end-of-season clash could at any moment come alive with Stan on the field. So obsessive was his craving for goals he could put us one up or one down at any minute!

Crowds during the decade declined steadily. As with many non-League clubs, Athletico had to compete with more illustrious neighbours – Spurs, Liverpool, Plymouth and Celtic. All were within a 500-mile radius of Whaddon, and many misguided soccer fans preferred travelling to those grounds rather than succumb to the semi-pro subtleties on show at 'The Tip'.

Wally Smott's mediocrity raised him above many of the managers who guided the club over the years, but Athletico

reserved a bottom six position from 1951 to 1955 and Ken
Mentle's dream of League football became a nightmare.

During a heated board meeting in June 1955, Wally
announced he was 'Going outside for a fag. I might be some
time.'

Three narrow and thoroughly encouraging defeats (1–0,
5–0, 9–0) kicked off the 55/56 season and raffle winner Sid
Beamish found himself at the helm. It was revealed many
years later that Sid had not actually bought the winning
ticket but had found it mysteriously floating in his half-time
Bovril.

What could have proved a disastrous appointment did, and
Athletico were only saved from oblivion by the inspired
choice of Reg Pybus as coach. Reg was already a well
respected backroom boy and came to the club from high-
flying Walborough Solid Fuel Albion. Why he decided to drop

Coach Reg Pybus in 1957

three divisions and stay with the club until his first dismissal in 1987, remains shrouded in slipped fivers. Scurrilous newspaper allegations over the years have hinted at blackmail, involving an unsavoury incident in the Walborough shower, forged Sheffield Wednesday rosettes and a second-hand Ford Popular Reg sold to Ken Mentle in 1954.

Whatever his reasons for staying, Reg certainly knew his football and it was he who turned a team of no-hopers into one capable of sustaining a bottom six position for the rest of the decade. By the end of the 59/60 campaign, a new optimism had arrived. Beamish was slowly grasping his newfound trade and, with Pybus at his side, players and supporters saw the coming season as the dawning of a new age.

The Swinging Sixties swung into action with a 4–1 defeat on Boxing Day and the sacking of Sid Beamish just before Redland Park Avenue's third goal.

The quart bottle of Nettles scheduled for first prize in the raffle was replaced by the top job and the winning ticket, always known on these occasions as 'Ken's shilling', went to Norvm Homstat. Unlike his predecessors, Norvm had managerial experience, having formerly held the reins at Railway Sidings Malmo. Obviously, his appointment was a fix but the Homstat-Pybus partnership was seen as a surefire recipe for success.

Homstat's grasp of football management was considerable, his grasp of English nil. Not only that, but he refused to leave Sweden and would commute by Volvo, North Sea Ferry and British Rail.

With the world's transport systems not prepared to align themselves with Athletico training sessions or match kick-offs, Homstat was sometimes absent for weeks on end, giving team talks with the aid of an interpreter over the telephone, or he would be a lone, pathetic figure, sat in the dug-out on a wet Monday morning urging on thin air.

Perhaps it was the need for stability to offset the 'Whads'

sterility but, remarkably, Homstat remained with the club until 1968. He refused to compromise in any way and, throughout his long association with the club, only mastered two words in English, both of which he frequently practised on referees. After numerous bookings he was banned from the touchline, banned from the grandstand the following season and, in his last season with the club, directed play, in Swedish, from the car park with the aid of a megaphone.

His astronomical travelling expenses all but bankrupted the club, and his non-appearance at over half the games sapped team morale. Further financial difficulties arose when he signed Swedish quadruplets Hans, Benny, Bjorn and Agnetha Larsson. The fact that they were considered for the Swedish national side in 1965 cut no ice with discerning Athletico fans. During that period of Swedish football, you could get in the national squad by postal application.

Left to right: Swedish starlets Benny, Agnetha, Bjorn (top) and Hans

The brothers also refused to give up seal culling between October and April and were seen at 'The Tip' even less than the manager. Naturally, with a weakened squad for so much of the season, Athletico's promotion challenge had to wait but, sinking deeper into debt, it came as no surprise when Homstat's contract was flushed down the loo and the Larssons were told they were no longer fjordable.

So 1968/69 loomed and Reg Pybus seemed the natural choice to take over as manager. But a boardroom vote of six to one in favour was not enough to secure him the position. Ken Mentle, who often made up club rules as he went along, declared that his was the casting vote and promptly blocked the appointment, incredibly naming himself as manager.

Fans were stunned and Pybus' resignation was expected before the start of the new season. However, after a lively meeting with directors, Reg was persuaded to carry on as coach by three men in a hearse who asked to meet him outside during a beer break.

By the opening game, a rare 2–2 draw with Racing Club Barnesfield, Mentle had sacked himself. Continually fighting in and out the dug-out, bickering over team selection and a 1954 Ford Popular, the Mentle/Pybus partnership was completely unworkable. With Ken's second-hand car business booming – 'turn the clock back with Mentle Motors' – he was happy to relieve command.

Dynamic accountant Julian Ripley-Rust came in as team manager and commercial adviser to the club. Rust had good financial credentials and the requisite limited knowledge of football. Desperate for cash following the Swedish debacle, he was one of the first to take on commercial sponsorship by negotiating a less than lucrative deal with Lovetts Panty Hose Ltd, and solely responsible for the bankrupting record fiasco when, at crippling expense, the team took on the guise of the Whaddon Promotion All Stars, and released a record, *Go Go Athletic-O*.

On Saturdays we turn out in our yellow and black strip,
To the chantin' of the faithful few down at 'The Tip'.
There's always lots of action tho' football is a plus,
We've never been to Wembley but we've seen it from a
     bus.

Go Go Go Athletico,
Go Go Go Go for goal.
They say we are the turkeys but you better believe,
We'll be doing all the stuffing,
In the Mid-Counties Combination League.

The record, many copies of which still turn up among the ditches and hedgerows at the leafier end of Whaddon, portrayed a hope and optimism belied by bailiffs at the turnstiles, and its hummability led players and supporters to see the coming season and decade as the dawning of a new age.

LES IN CONFIDENCE

MONDAY, 5th OCTOBER

Trying to compose myself, before concocting the programme notes for the Gosling Celtic match, I notice that I have developed a bad case of the shakes. This may, of course, be due to alcoholic withdrawal but then again perhaps it is a nervous reaction to the hell of this past week.

Those scumbags at the Public Health office sprang an inspector on us last Wednesday. Despite the fact that the showers were writhing with the flabby excesses of Whaddon British Legion 'B' and Mitchley Fire Brigade Dynamoes, this idiot insisted on carrying out his inspection. I thought it a touch of inspiration on my part insisting that he remove all his clothing, 'in the interests of hygiene'. Naturally I never thought the daft sod would, and so there was nothing for it, I had to do likewise and follow him, à la buff, into the showers. The whole thing was a total bloody fiasco. As if the stench of stale sweat and stagnant liniment was not enough, I had to endure the grotesque sensation of his sodden sodding notepad disintegrating between my toes. Luckily, despite the cramped conditions, I was able to block the inspector's view, thereby obscuring Colin Webley's neanderthal plumbing and the various cultures and mould growths my boy Chester has been propagating on the water tank as part of his Tech. college project on legionnaires disease.

Unluckily, neither the inspector nor myself spotted the stray soap and after slipping arse over tit he put his head through the water tank. At this point the rusty trough decided to spew out gallons of ice cold water, panic ensued and 24 naked men made a rush for the exit, much to the astonishment of those still lingering on the touchline after the Wednesday League match.

Was it any wonder I resorted to the drinks cabinet in the director's Portakabin? I only had a couple. A couple of whiskies, a couple of vodkas and a couple of swigs of embrocation. Now, I can hold my liquor as well as the next man, so it is ludicrous to suggest that when I reversed the club van into the tea hut I was under the influence. It was a delusion I was under. What with the shower incident and the strain of management I neglected to recall the fact I could not drive. A simple enough mistake. Anyway, to be on the safe side I have not touched a drop since, but God knows the temptation has been great. Pahdra Singh called me to the club this morning where he and Reg Pybus and their crony, that stingy git Pugh, the corpse planter, unveiled the new team strip. Gawd help us, no wonder the launch was 'shrouded' in mystery: the last time I saw those shirts they were wrapped around the kneelers in Mitchley Crematorium!

REMEMBER: TAKE CHESTER TO THE VET.

ATHLETICO WHADDON

M/SV. DIVISION 3.

TODAY
. V .
REDLAND PARK AVENUE

£1

✳ OFFICIAL PROGRAMME ✳

	P	W	D	L	PTS
ALBORNE	10	6	1	3	19
NORTHTOWN	10	5	3	2	18
GOSLING CELTIC	10	5	3	2	18
REDLAND PARK AVENUE	10	4	4	2	16
CLANSFORD UTD	10	4	4	2	16
FRAMPTON ROVERS	10	4	3	3	15
HELLINGBOROUGH	10	4	2	4	14
FELTON	10	4	1	5	13
DORNING TOWN	10	3	4	3	13
ATH. WHADDON	10	4	1	5	13
SCRIMLEY ARSENAL	10	3	3	4	12
SPORTING HYDRA CHEMICALS	10	2	5	3	11
TWITCHIT ALBION	10	2	4	4	10
LEECH TOWN	10	2	4	4	10
BOTHAM WDRS	10	3	1	6	10
CHAMDEN CITY RESERVES	10	2	3	5	9
SIDCOMBE	10	2	3	5	9

MANAGER'S NOTES

7th November '92

A month is a very long tim in fotbal. It was over for weeks ago that we last publishd a programe, as finansises have been moch two tite for such extragavance.

During this tim the teem hav kept up sum kind of consisstincy by continuwing to loose more games than it haz one. the won-O rouncing by Gozling Celtick was particlely dissappointting tho perhaps no unxpeckeded. Owr unlucky 4-too defeet at Northtown was overshaded by the second sendingoff this season 4 Trever Probe after an hi kicking insident, in which the refereez jaw was broken.

This was only owr fift defeet in ten leeg games (we allso went don 2– at Clansford) so it stood us in good sted for owr Fst rownd match against Drizley Welfare in the 'FARMBOY SHEEP SCAB LINEMENT INTER-LEAGUE TROPHY'. Money of yew will agree that this was owr best proformance of the season so there an owne goal by Davedoyle rite from the kockiff was not a good start but too superherb hedders from Royston Marlee, playing with hevily bandiged neez, one the day four us.

Thowz of u hoo followed us to Hemlock Valley Crusaders for round two must like me. Have espeariensed a sense of day-o shavu as daveDoyle poot the Crusaders ahed with another of hiz cracking owne goles. This tim however we was unabel to mustard owr yewshul gravel and detriment and so went out thre30–.

*　　　　*　　　　*　　　　*　　　　*

Spiking of losses Colin Webley, the club kipper has now returned to his favorit posishun behind the T-counter. Colin

Who, only took up fotbal this seeson has licked nothin in yuthanasium (110$ purr mach) but sadlee could not adap to this hi standard of footee.

* * * * *** * *

May I tak this opoortuneity to silence those dictators of owr acting person Mr. PD Sing. No yes Mr Singe is dedicated to the fewcher of Athletes Whaddon and to proove it has prezented me with a BLANK czech for £53–24p only, which is at my dispozal for strainthning the squid.
WELL DON MR SINHG

* * * 1*

Thow owr leeg campain is priority I have a snee king feeling that this year could be owr year for cup gory. Wee begin owr long March to Wimble wembley next tuesday when we take on hifiying Clutton Town in the preliminary liminary first Qualifying Round of the Fa cup. Kikkup 3 70 a.m.

* * ********

Finale may I xtend a heart felt wellcome back to owr chairman Mr. Kin Mental. Tho still farr from competent a 110£ recovery Ken returns today to his beloved Tipp and know dobt the familyer sound of his ukelelelele will be unentertaining us wonse more at halftime. WELL COME BACK SODN.

Thanx mussed also go to the Mitchley Road Primary Skool printing clubb four taking over the produckshun of owr programe. I hope the yungstirs do not hav much dribble with the difficult wurds.

LEZ BONCE

SPOTLIGHT ON ATHLETICO
WHADDON 1970–1979

Athletico Whaddon (1970) Ltd rose from the cheque books of Ken Mentle and Julian Ripley-Rust. The team that ended the 1960s was dumped, and Ripley-Rust and Pybus set about the daunting task of building a squad capable of winning promotion when the club's League career got underway again.

As a result of their financial difficulties, Athletico were forced to resign from the Mid-Counties League and for the 70/71 season played no football at all, thereby suffering no defeats and thus securing their most successful season ever.

Matchless, they spent the season to good effect, scouring the reserve benches of Swansons Sweet Pickle Albion and their ilk. By July they had managed to sign a nucleus of nine players and re-applied to join the Mid-Counties League. However, by some strange quirk of FA paperwork they found themselves in the Multivite Vegeburger/Singletons Valve Replacement League, formerly the Mid-Counties South-West (Northern Division) whose Premier Division Athletico had briefly graced in 1938.

So, as the 71/72 season dawned, Athletico found themselves with a new team, a new league and a bright future. Their opening fixture was a home match against Potley Town and the club decided that this was the day to wake up Whaddon to its new go-ahead football team.

At 2.30p.m. in the Fine Fare car park, a procession mustered. The Whaddon and Mitchley Scouts and Guides band wound its tuneless way along the High Street, followed by six young girls lethally wielding pom-poms – the Mentle Motors Majorettes – and bringing up the rear, Reg Pybus' Bedford minibus in which, crammed like sardines, the new team sat invisible behind the heavily steamed up windows.

Owing to faulty traffic lights at the top of Tip Lane, the procession was held up and, on arriving at the ground, found Potley already on the pitch and themselves a hefty fine for their late arrival for the game. To cap this day of celebration, the 'Whads' went down 4–0 and manager Julian Ripley-Rust was sacked.

Reg took over as caretaker-manager but after only ten minutes of their second match realised that Athletico were out of their depth in Division One and, sure enough, the club was bundled into the Second, finishing the season fifteen points adrift at the bottom.

Pybus was duly sacked but retained as club coach in a refreshment-making capacity. As season 72/73 arrived, a passing shopper, Mrs Hilda Sheppey (58), suddenly found herself the first manageress in football history. Hilda, known affectionately as the 'blue rinse boss', was, to everyone's surprise, to enjoy three seasons in charge at 'The Tip'. Under her direction, the squad became a very close-knit affair comprising as it did four cousins, six nephews and a younger brother (42). The core of the team remained virtually unchanged throughout her reign: Sheppey, Holt, Sheppey, Rawlings, Sheppey, Rawlings, Rawlings, Sheppey, Sheppey, Rawlings, Von Bopp.

Despite a certain amount of success, including a best-ever tenth in the league (73/74), when the board decided to switch training from Tuesday to Thursday Hilda was forced to resign, as it would clash with her night out at bingo.

Once more Reg Pybus was given command and many believed he had inherited one of the great Whaddon sides. Unfortunately, the discovery that young, vivacious, Tania Sheppey was about to enter motherhood, courtesy of centre-half Brian Rawlings, brought about a family rivalry that spilled over on to the football pitch, notably during a League game against Thornham Bridge.

Sheppey A., Sheppey K., Rawlings P., Rawlings B., and Von Bopp were sent off for fighting amongst themselves along with Thornham Bridge captain (later with Athletico), Trevor Proby, who hit everybody. Surprisingly the remaining 'Whads', Holt T., Sheppey S., Rawlings G., Sheppey R., Sheppey V., and Rawlings D., held out to secure an astonishing 2–0 draw in the Bridge's favour.

After such an intolerable display, all those involved in the incident were sacked and Reg Pybus was left to rebuild as best he could.

Over the next few seasons debts continued to mount and in an unprecedented move Athletico again made history, becoming the first club to introduce the £1 pork pie. The players also felt the pinch. A proposed cut in wages was doubled, they were charged 25 pence for the half-time orange and were required to leave a £35 deposit when they took their kit home for washing.

Somehow, despite his regular sacking, Reg managed to keep the club in Division Two. In 77/78 he relinquished the hot seat to former Grundle Ferry Dynamo boss, Roy Alderman, and then the following season to Rabbi Lionel Cohen, who never attended a Saturday match on religious grounds. But by the end of the decade he was once more in charge.

Unable to pay his playing staff, crisis followed crisis but as the 1980s arrived, dramatic changes were about to unfold. These changes were seen by players and supporters alike as the dawning of a new age.

SPOTLIGHT ON THE SUPPORTERS' CLUB

As anyone involved in football knows, the backbone of a good team is a good manager (Matt Busby, Kenny Dalglish, Les Bence). The dynamic diaphragm of any club, however, is its support, those diehards who, for no reward, man the gates, pick up litter, kick back the divots and aerosol the toilets. These are the dedicated few who, week in, week out, come rain or snow, stare out of the clubhouse window at 22 diehards freezing their pads off for fun.

Athletico formed its own official Supporters' Club in 1953. It was founded by Stan Barnet and Sid Dicker and in the early days met behind the grandstand on match days. They gained a permanent home in 1961 when the groundsman's hut became vacant. Unfortunately, it could only accommodate six people and a crate of Nettles Agricultural Sherry so, as membership grew, tempers were often explosive and much precious nectar was spilt.

The turning point came in 1972 when Ken Mentle dug deep into his pocket and bought a deluxe Portakabin for directors and players, and the Supporters' Club was given the drain end as its new home. This move brought players and fans into regular contact, and the board presented one young supporter, Leslie Bence, with life membership after he was spotted by the team at an away match.

It was not long before the club became a social 'Mecca' for the local community. Bingo, skittles, old-tyme Kung-fu, spitting at the chicken, all ensured that the club's calendar was full for 370 days a year. There have been many great events to remember over the years. The 1976 Open Blow-Football Tournament, won by a crack Whaddon WI team, springs to mind, as does the 1974 Christmas jumble sale which received a four-star review in the Oxfam magazine.

Then who can forget those cabaret evenings? Remember topless rock and roll with Victor Shrigley and his Giggly Wigglies. Bottomless sing-a-longs with Bob Sedgemoor and his organ, or those popular Country and Western evenings with Whaddon's own 'Belle of the Canteena', Rosetta Fish, or the singing house conveyors, Deceptively Spacious Tex Mortgage and the Black Gulch Estate Agents.

Yes, when it comes to social events, the Athletico Supporters' Club can feel rightly proud.

Rev. V. Shrigley
Soc. Sec.

LES IN CONFIDENCE

THURSDAY, 5th NOVEMBER

I have just taken a long, stiff drink. About a litre long and as stiff as Liberace. I warned the board that privatising the programme production would be a disaster. Scully and Sons have had the job for as long as I can remember, not because they are any good but because they are ruddy cheap. Old man Scully has not put his prices up since 1947 and he probably bought his printing set from John Bull himself. It was Pybus who had the brilliant idea of putting the thing out to tender and, despite my warnings, thought that no one could match the school's price of 158 banana chews, free strawberry milkshakes once a week during the season and a promise from Mike Channon that he would play the Virgin Mary in the school nativity play. Well, Reg and Singh were very quiet when I showed them what those little brats had produced. Hells bells! they could not even spell teem! We managed to salvage the Spotlight feature but my bloody notes had already been printed. They had nothing for it but to crawl back to Mr Scully and to pay Mike Channon's cancellation fee (£353) out of their own pockets.

If this club wants to know how to make money then it ought to listen to my boy Chester. At his suggestion we will be holding a car boot sale at 'The Tip' in the near future. He tells me that it is a dead cert, we can make an absolute killing by taking a percentage of the profits, and charging pitch holders a rip-off rent. Details have still to be worked out, but Chez reckons that with the aid of his home computer and his Nintendo Boot Sale Blitz game, he and I can milk off a tidy sum whilst still leaving the club with a small profit. It is good to see Chester growing up in my image. I have noticed how close we have grown since his mother ran off with the Turnbury Post Office United's physiotherapist.

This boot sale is such a good idea I think I might have my own pitch and run a Help The Aged stall. I am sure I could sting this town's senile pensioners for a couple of quid, by selling them the old tea hut as firewood. It would certainly get it out of the back of my Reliant. After the fiasco over the programmes I shall take full control of this project and set up my headquarters in the Jessie Matthews Lounge at the Duck and Forceps.

Colin Webley called round earlier at my request. I decided to be tactful and told him he would no longer be considered for the team because he is complete and utter rubbish. I told him there were no hard feelings and that I was only thinking of the club, blah, blah, blah. To soften the blow I said it was only because I was held in such high esteem in the football world that I had to get rid of any player or, as in his case, friend, who showed any sign of being a no-hoper. It was my duty to nurture and encourage only those with potential and he had about as much as a Mike Channon betting tip.

Webley was visibly shocked but I assured him he could still continue to wash the team strip every week.

I am just an old softie at heart.

ATHLETICO WHADDON

M/SV. DIVISION 3

TODAY

.V.

SIDCOMBE

£1

* OFFICIAL PROGRAMME *

	P	W	D	L	PTS
CLANSFORD UTD	16	9	4	3	31
GOSLING CELTIC	16	8	5	3	29
ALBORNE	16	7	5	4	26
SCRIMLEY ARSENAL	16	7	4	5	25
NORTHTOWN	16	7	4	5	25
HELLINGBOROUGH	16	7	3	6	24
REDLAND PARK AVENUE	16	6	6	4	24
FRAMPTON ROVERS	16	6	4	6	22
LEECH TOWN	16	5	6	5	21
SPORTING HYDRA CHEMICALS	16	5	5	6	20
TWITCHIT ALBION	16	5	4	7	19
BOTHAM WDRS	16	6	1	9	19
FELTON	15	5	3	7	18
DORNING TOWN	15	4	6	5	18
CHAMDEN CITY RESERVES	16	3	5	8	14
ATH. WHADDON	14	4	1	9	13
SIDCOMBE	16	2	6	8	12

MANAGER'S NOTES

16th January '93

Welcome back to 'The Tip', everybody.

The reasons for our absence over the last month or more have been well documented in the local gutter press, and through the many acrimonious exchanges between club and supporters. Back at the beginning of November we instigated our first car boot sale, which we reluctantly accept was less than a 110 per cent success. Heavy rain the night before meant the pitch was waterlogged, and a misunderstanding between the groundsman and myself led to his directing all vehicles on to the playing area. Many of these cars had to be towed off by a tractor which, like our forward line, itself became bogged down in midfield. With the pitch resembling a motocross track, we had no option but to postpone our home games with Dorning Town and Felton. This resulted in a hefty fine being imposed by the county FA, on top of a fine for fielding an ineligible player during the match at Twitchit Albion.

Once again our chairman, Mr Ken Mentle, has been called upon to bale us out but, unlike the current state of our penalty area, his wallet is not a bottomless pit.

*　　　*　　　*　　　*　　　*　　　*　　　*

When you witness the amount of effort and skill our lads ignite every match with, it is astonishing that our League results in our absence from 'The Tip' have been a string of defeats. Losing 1–0, 5–3 and 2–0 to Redland Park Avenue, Botham Wanderers, and Twitchit Albion respectively means that promotion may now be beyond our grasp.

Yet these results seem quite astonishing if you cast your mind back to our last appearance at 'The Tip'. It was then that we took on the giants of the Premier Division, Clutton Town, in the FA Cup. They left 'The Tip' if you recall, with egg on their faces after securing a pitiful 6–2 victory over us. Many Clutton players and supporters were still stunned by Royston Marley's brilliant brace of goals as they boarded the bus home. I am sure you are all aware that Royston is an important cog in the Athletico jigsaw and his recurrent knee injury has played a large part in our poor results this season. On behalf of the club, I have approached Ross Chicken Ltd in the hope that 'Royst' may be relieved from his job as a chicken sexer and a more 'knee-friendly' task found for him.

*   *   *   *   *   *   *

Such is the lot of the football manager that constant criticism has to be lived with. Recently, my managerial integrity has been called into question by a number of directors and supporters. Their concern relates to my dismissing the former club captain, Colin Webley. After many years dispensing tea to supporters, Colin took up football with the club this season and, to boost his confidence, I appointed him skipper. After six competitive games it became clear to me that the standard of football required in the Multivite/Singletons League Division Three was way beyond his ability and so, sadly, I felt the club was no longer able to accommodate him as a player. I am as surprised as anyone to learn that Colin has now signed for current Football League champions Leeds United.

Since this news broke, I have been subjected to numerous snide remarks concerning my ability to spot a footballer when I see one. Let me make it clear, football is a game played by one team against another with a ball. It requires planning, skill and tactics to create a winning side and if the individual players do not fit into the maze, if they cannot work within a cohesive unit, then success will elude the whole team. With limited resources I am striving to build a ruthless goal-scoring machine. There is no place for a quality footballer if he believes he is more than just a page in that machine. No individual, apart from myself, is bigger than this club.

*   *   *   *   *   *   *

Although results are running against us, surely today, against bottom club Sidcombe, who narrowly defeated us 3–0 earlier this season, we can record our fifth win of the present campaign.

SPOTLIGHT ON ATHLETICO WHADDON 1980–1992

1980 brought yet another new manager in Ken Smith, local farmer and playboy. Smith's first task was to improve the ground's facilities. Plans were put into action to buy and erect floodlights, but more importantly to install toilets, as the constant 'watering' of the oak tree behind the grandstand was causing it to rot away and sway, menacingly, over the directors' seats. Regrettably, Ken Mentle handed over the money to Smith and, as well as manager, appointed him club development officer. By the time it was discovered that Smith had used the money to develop the bank accounts of local bookies and the jewellery collections of local ladies of ill repute, it was too late. The club managed to recoup £304, and this was spent on a single floodlight. Smith's dismissal put Reg Pybus back in charge for the rest of the season, the undoubted highlight of which was a special match held to celebrate the turning on of the floodlight. Athletico took on the toughest of opposition by playing a Darlington Groundstaff XI. The Mayor, Ivor Cuth, placed the last of 150 U2 batteries in position, and the light was switched on. A magnificent crowd of 83 witnessed the ceremony, 32 of them staying for the match. The event started with a slight hiccup when it was discovered that the batteries were in the wrong way round. Play around the centre spot was fast and furious, though the ground was in total darkness everywhere else. The game was abandoned after fifteen minutes when the ball disappeared in a black hole at the sewage works end.

After another year languishing, knee high, in Division Two, Reg was once again ousted and, for season 82/83, fanatical big mouth and stalwart supporter, Vic Noodle, took over.

Originally, he was on a six-month contract but despite disappointing results he was able to re-negotiate his contract. He married Yvonne Mentle, Ken's daughter. Vic Noodle kicked off married life and the new season by pawning his wife's jewellery and bringing in a clutch of new signings. Although slow and the wrong side of 43, 'Gabby' Hinton was classy and a strong believer in football and family entertainment. To this end, he often smoked his pipe during the game and always insisted on playing in his slippers. Another colourful signing was the Reverend Hubert Jolly, who followed in the footsteps of that other great sporting cleric, W. G. Grace, although W. G. was a cricketer not a footballer and a doctor not a vicar. Jolly was already a well known celebrity, not only for his pre-match evangelising but also for his best-selling books on clerical life, *Vicars in a Twist* and *Bare Butts in the Belfry*. On the field he was extremely competent, having spent years in the forward line of St Dodimeads Choirboys XI and the Billy Graham Crusade. Later he became a director of the club and built the small chapel behind the groundsman's hut where visiting supporters could find 'quiet contemplation and a cup of Bovril (58p)'.

The most notable of Vic's signings, however, was former Thornham Bridge captain, Trevor Proby. Desperate for players, Athletico were willing to take a chance with Proby and his fiery temper. This was Noodle's big mistake. In thirty outings during the season, Proby's vicious streak, and obsessive belief that all referees were illegitimate, led to him receiving his marching orders no less than eighteen times!

Aware of Trevor's previous record, the FA sentenced him to a 152-match suspension, a ban of four years. Whereas in management I take the raw clay of inexperience, then shape and mould it into a team of teapots, Vic had an old-fashioned approach, plucking players with natural ability and building them into a cohesive unit but where no player's unique, individual flair was stifled. His third and final term opened with

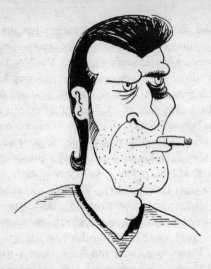

Hard man Trevor Proby reacts philosophically to his four-match ban

great success. Although Whaddon were the only team to enter, and despite the FA declaring the competition null and void, we can, in all fairness I think, claim to have been holders of the Charwoods' Sweet Pickle A and B Cup. That season also saw our best ever run in the FA Cup, reaching the second preliminary, preliminary qualifying round before bowing out 4–0 to Ajax Pan-Shine Combination League champions, Amblewick Carthegians. Good League results led even the club's sternest critic to believe that in Vic Noodle we had found the man to take us into the Football League. Then disaster struck. The *Whaddon and Mitchley Argus*, under the by-line of trainee reporter-cyclist Mark Crowe, revealed that Yvonne Noodle (*née* Mentle), had been carrying on an affair with disgraced Athletico player, Trevor Proby. The paper published photographs, taken by Crowe, from a distance of half a mile, that purported to be of a topless Trevor and a scantily overcoated Yvonne sucking toes on the lawn of

Proby's Thornham Bridge hacienda. Ken Mentle was placed in an awkward situation but saw his loyalties as lying with his daughter. Unbelievably, he sacked his son-in-law and replaced him in the manager's seat with Trevor Proby. This news rocked the Whaddon footballing fraternity and questions were even asked in the house, albeit the Duck and Forceps public house.

Fate, however, now played a striker's role. Trevor was unable to take up his post because, through circumstances beyond the law, he was forced to lie low in the Bahamas for a couple of years. But the damage had been done. Despite free lunches, unlimited use of Ken's chauffeur-driven Lada and the promise of regular wages, Vic Noodle declined the chance to return. Instead he took up a lucrative coaching post with the Botswana Youth team. There was no Reg Pybus to stand in this time, he too had left for pastures new. Manager of Third Division Bowden Mesopotamians.

Pensioner Walter Niblet pulled the dreaded raffle ticket from the bucket to become manager for season 87/88. I personally led a vigorous campaign to get Niblet removed at the first opportunity. I lambasted the board through the letters page of the 'Sporting Mauve' for appointing an octogenarian ignoramus. Sadly, the momentum gathered in the early days of my crusade had fizzled out by April, when it became obvious we were heading for Division One. As it was, my criticism was entirely vindicated. A disastrous run of one defeat in nine games meant we ended the season a pathetic third. Against my advice, Walter, despite being 78, was immediately named manager for 88/89 and this time we were runners-up and promoted.

It was a proud day for 'The Tip' when the dawning of the 89/90 season saw us amongst the Multivite/Singletons élite. That first season back in Division One is still fondly recalled by supporters. Some of the players have already passed into Whaddon's sporting folklore. Names like Dalglish, Gascgoine and Shilton, three jewels in Athletico's crown, are always mentioned in reverential tones on the terraces or in the Anna Neagle Grill and Burger Bar at the Duck and Forceps. Melvin Dalglish, our tussle-haired goalkeeper who had Velcro stuck to the palms of his gloves. Stanley Gascgoine, a green marvel with a two-pronged attack, left foot, right foot or head. Ivor Shilton, a midfield dynamo whose nose glowed in the dark.

Finding the workload too much, 'Nibby' coaxed Reg Pybus back as his assistant, but when Walter Niblet dropped dead during a 3–1 defeat by Red Star Onglethorpe, Ken refused to appoint Reg as caretaker manager. Instead, he put the job back in the raffle. This was to be a momentous decision although he did not know it at the time. With the club now languishing at the bottom of the table they were in desperate need of a football visionary, a new footballing messiah. They needed a miracle and that miracle was me, Les Bence. A life-long supporter, I have always been regarded as a tactical genius by the Duck and Forceps regulars and, from day one, my appointment has brought renewed hope to the terraces.

During my term as manager I have made few friends and my enemies stalk the boardroom in ever increasing numbers. I have survived only on the fantastic loyalty of players and fans. Their loyalty has stayed with me because, despite the disappointment of relegation in 90/91 and our meteoric plummet through Division Two last season, they know that I can in no way be held responsible.

In actual fact, throughout the entire history of Athletico Whaddon, much of the blame for our failure can be placed at the feet of one man, Ken Mentle. Far be it from me to speak ill of the dead but Ken Mentle, may he rest in peace, single-handedly made this club what it is today, the Accrington Stanley of Bradford Park Avenue.

Thank heavens we at last have at the helm a manager of exceptional gifts and a fabulous chairman, Mr Pahdra Singh, who has no interest in soccer. Football needs more men like

Pahdra at the masthead. It needs men who are willing, without question, to say, 'I'll leave it up to you, Les, whatever you say.'

All Pahdra and I require is unquestioning encouragement and support. If we get this, then I see the 1990s as the dawning of a new age for Athletico Whaddon.

LES IN CONFIDENCE

WEDNESDAY, 13th JANUARY 1993

As I sat down to write up my diary a brick arrived through my sitting room window. The window was closed. It is now open. The brick was wrapped in two notes, the first apologised for the mess and the second, bearing Trevor Proby's signature, offered to lend me the £250 the club are still trying to stitch me for after that car boot sale fiasco. I am going to have to take Proby up on his offer but Gawd knows what the interest will be.

Athletico are nothing but money-grabbing bastards. All right, so I took full responsibility for the organisation of the sale, but there is no way I can be blamed for the outcome. As I told the board before their meeting with the Receiver, the blame lies solely with the person who dreamt up the idea, namely Chester Bence. They were not impressed. Still, it taught me a thing or two. For one thing, it is about time that little sod Chester started paying rent to live here — £250 seems to be the going rate these days. He treats this place like a dressing room, him and his groundhopping mates. Hardly a day goes by without being neck-high in severely anoraked shop assistants, munching Kit-Kats and watching endless slides of football ground urinals from the length and breadth of Britain. If it's not them, then the house is buried in thousands of paper slips on which he works out leagues and fixtures for his absurd postal blow-football competition.

Things are becoming intolerable at the club these days and the boot sale is only part of it. Our abysmal form has brought calls for my resignation, notably from fatty Singh and his toady Pybus, but also from many supporters. I do not think Ken Mentle's support will survive his clogged arteries. I shall make it clear to those moronic malcontents on the terraces that I have no intention of quitting. I shall bluff it out at least until my next dole cheque. These people seem to forget that results do not mean a thing in football and are only of secondary interest to a manager. In my book the only time a manager should consider resigning is when he starts believing his own programme notes. What these boardroom blouses and toerags at the turnstiles do not realise is that football management is not a skill to be acquired through hard work, but a gift from God. Those blessed with a prophetic vision of soccer's future, like Mike Channon and myself, are often completely ignored or misunderstood, whereas charlatans who would not know one end of a football from another, the Reg Pybuses and Howard Wilkinsons of this world, suck up to mediocrity and call it talent.

When Piedish told me he had secured Webley's transfer to Leeds United, I laughed him out of the Duck and Forceps. It is a joke and I told Wilkinson so. In fact, so contemptible did I find his dismissal of my judgement as to what constitutes talent on the football field, that I flatly refused the £200,000 fee they were willing to pay for Colin Webley and let the useless git go on a free transfer!

REMEMBER: NAME TREV PROBY AS NEW CAPTAIN.

ATHLETICO WHADDON

M/SV. DIVISION 3

TODAY
· V ·
CHAMDEN CITY RESERVES

£1

✳ OFFICIAL PROGRAMME ✳

	P	W	D	L	PTS
CLANSFORD UTD	18	11	4	3	37
GOSLING CELTIC	18	9	5	4	32
NORTHTOWN	18	8	5	5	29
SCRIMLEY ARSENAL	18	8	4	6	28
HELLINGBOROUGH	18	8	3	7	27
ALBORNE	18	7	6	5	27
REDLAND PARK AVENUE	18	6	7	5	25
TWITCHIT ALBION	18	7	4	7	25
SPORTING HYDRA CHEMICALS	18	6	6	6	24
LEECH TOWN	18	6	6	6	24
FRAMPTON ROVERS	18	6	5	7	23
FELTON	17	6	3	8	21
DORNING TOWN	17	5	6	6	21
CHAMDEN CITY RESERVES	18	5	5	8	20
BOTHAM WDRS	18	6	2	10	20
SIDCOMBE	18	3	6	9	15
ATH. WHADDON	16	4	1	11	13

MANAGER'S NOTES

30th January '93

Ken Mentle, a 'Stiff' to the end

It is with deep regret that, on behalf of Athletico Whaddon Football Club, I have to report the death of club chairman, Mr Ken Mentle. Forty-two years as a devoted servant to this club is an astonishing record and Ken's dedication to and belief in Athletico is an example to everyone in the world of football. The loss to the game, through his sad departure to that great boardroom in the sky, is incalculable. Ken's enthusiasm never diminished and up until his recent heart trouble his work rate for the club was never less than 114 per cent. Ironically, he was on the way to a full recovery when he choked on a curry bone at acting chairman, Mr Pahdra Singh's, restaurant. Although still in a state of shock, Mr

Singh has now appointed himself to the full chairmanship and, along with myself, represented the club at the funeral. Mr Singh's appointment was unanimously approved by the board following the resignation of long-time directors, taxi owner Fred Tilley and poodle manicurist Raymonde Carter. Their positions have now been filled by Mr Namadra Singh and Mr Giljod Singh, neither of whom, surprisingly, are related to the chairman.

*　　　*　　　*　　　*　　　*　　　*　　　*

Chairman Singh's cash injection of £53.24, back in November, has brought no less than FOUR new players to the club. Clive Smott (59) was formerly with Princess Eugene Road Garage Reserves and has agreed to come out of retirement and put on his boots for the first time in three years. Wayne Pollock (38) is a young, exciting defender who nevertheless believes, like me, in some of football's older values like neat hair and shorts down past his.knees. Darren Pugh is the nephew of Mr Pugh, partner in Lonsdale and Pugh, undertakers and, of course, our sponsors. This should assure him of a bright future with 'The Stiffs' and, in all probability, lead to the club captaincy next season. Darren, who is only thirteen and ineligible to play, looks seventeen and so should fool League officials. Finally, new boy number four, and our most exciting capture in years, Miguel Romerez (34). Miguel joins us direct from BARCELONA, where he lived for several months. The talented Spaniard has just opened a pizza parlour in the town and has not played football before. However, it is a well known fact that all Spanish men are born with a football in their mouth and so I am sure his dormant skills will blossom forth as soon as he walks out on to the park.

*　　　*　　　*　　　*　　　*　　　*　　　*

What an outstanding performance our home game with Sidcombe turned out to be a fortnight ago. We outclassed them in every department except one, goal-scoring, as their three to our none all too clearly showed. Many, like myself, thought we were unlucky to be the victims of Sidcombe's third victory of the season. At least it stood us in good stead for Tuesday night's game at Scrimley Arsenal, where we came away with a very creditable 2–4 defeat. Once again Royston Marley proved his class by netting both our goals with deflections off his deadly bottom. The amount of running he put in was quite remarkable when you remember that, on his doctor's advice, his knees were strapped together.

*　　　*　　　*　　　*　　　*　　　*　　　*

The foot of the League is beginning to take on a familiar appearance as far as Athletico is concerned:

	P	W	D	L	PTS
Chamden Res	18	5	5	8	20
Botham Wdrs	18	6	2	10	20
Sidcombe	18	3	6	9	15
Ath. Whaddon	16	4	1	11	13

However, I feel there is another way to look at it:

	P	W	D	L	PTS
Ath. Whaddon	16	4	1	11	13
Sidcombe	18	3	6	9	15
Botham Wdrs	18	6	2	10	20
Chamden Res	18	5	5	8	20

*　　　*　　　*　　　*　　　*　　　*　　　*

Today we entertain fellow strugglers, Chamden City Reserves, who we beat on the opening day of the season. They cannot match our record of ten defeats in a row, having staged something of a revival with three straight victories.

Following our disastrous Boxing Day at Leech Town (0–1) and equally poor start to the New Year, we are hoping for a turn in fortune today or, even at this late stage, postponement through frost.

YOUR LINE TO LES

Dear Leslie,

I am just a humble supporter who, though never blessed with the gift myself, loves the artistry and beauty of football and the poetry in motion displayed by the Athletico forward line.

I have often succumbed to the graceful, bronzed beauty of Michael Deere and Terence Wade's limbs as they power into action and imagine not John Motson or Alan Hansen commentating on another blistering attack, but David Attenborough in mildly hushed tones, comparing our boys with leaping gazelles or sprightly cheetahs. Do they affect you in the same way?

Yours, K.D.

Dear K.D.,

Gazelles? Cheetahs? How rare to find an aesthete and intellectual artisan, much like myself, on the terraces these days.

Too many people believe football is nothing more than a game, but you and I know it to be so much more. Somebody once said (Mick Channon?) that in the footballer's craft he saw 'The personification of nature in all its multivariant elements. The juxtaposition of art and realism, of beauty and brutality.' How true that is.

Throughout history football has been the favoured sport of the artistic community. As is well known, the Italians are soccer mad and so it is a fair bet that come Saturday, Michaelangelo would forsake the Cistern Chapel and Leonardo Di Vinci break off from designing the clockwork egg slicer and instead be found occupying the terraces of Inter-Milan or Juventus.

Yours, Leslie 'Bragg' Bence

Dear Les,

Let me come straight to the point. I am not a person to beat about the bush. I like to say what I have to say in as few words as possible and to lay my cards on the table for all to see. Terry Wade, get rid of him, Les.

Now I have nothing against Terry as a person, although I do not think I would cross the road to help him if he were run over by a lorry, but that is neither here nor there. It is the football that counts and frankly, me and the other two regulars are not impressed.

Somebody once said, I think it was you, Les, that football is all about attitude. We do not like Terry's. It is not for the likes of us to try and tell you your job, after all, you are the boss and it is your decision as to who gets in the squad, but when rubbish like Terry becomes a regular, well . . . it reflects on the whole team and your lousy judgement in particular. It will, I know, be a tough decision for you to make, Les, because it is common knowledge that Terry has you in his back pocket, but he is the weak link in the team this year. The round peg in a square forward line. He has to be dropped. Surely you can tap the chairman for a few quid so we can buy someone half-decent.

> Yours faithfully,
> V. Wade (Mrs)

Dear Mrs Wade,

Just because unsubstantiated rumours abound that Terry's brother Ted occasionally supplies me with specialist literature from the Continent, it does not mean I am taking backhanders or looking favourably towards Terry when including him in the first team.

With respect, I see myself as a master craftsman, but even craftsmen need quality tools to produce a work of art. I see my job here at 'The Tip' as akin to building the Taj Mahal from scratch.

Yours-in-hope,
LES BENCE

Dear Les,

Although you have not been in the manager's seat very long, you have done nothing to alter my original opinion that your appointment makes about as much sense as the Charge of the Light Brigade.

I love this club and so only wish to offer encouragement. However, I enclose a petition signed by 11,000 inhabitants (95 per cent of the local population) demanding your resignation by second post today.

Good luck,
R. Pybus (no relation)

Dear Reg,

So it was your petition I signed the other day, was it?

Since receiving a copy I have scrutinised it with a fine toothpick and believe the whole thing to be completely bogus. Although our home gates of between 26 and 130 are the envy of many a Football League club, they only represent 0.25 per cent of those who put their names to your petition. People will sign anything, son.

In all my days as a Whaddon resident I do not recall a Descartes family in the neighbourhood and surely (please God) there cannot be two Keith Chegwins in the world?

What really sets this up as a fraud and complete load of tripe, is the ridiculous assumption on the part of the forger, that my entire squad of players would happily sign a document whose sole aim is to get me removed from the manager's seat.

THE BOSS

LES IN CONFIDENCE

WEDNESDAY, 27th JANUARY

My loyalty to Athletico amazes even me sometimes. Despite clashing with my dole day, I had no hesitation in forgoing it to attend Ken Mentle's funeral.

Like every other funeral I have attended, laughs were few and the weather was bloody awful. Things got off to a bad start anyway when my Reliant Robin was crushed by Pahdra Singh's Bentley as we jostled for a parking place. Things got very heated as I demanded he pay me full compensation. Singh refused, saying he had no idea there was a car already in the space, all he had seen was a Reliant. In the end we compromised, Singh apologised and I agreed to pay for repairs to his sidelight.

Looking back on it, perhaps it was not appropriate for me to heckle the vicar over the inadequate parking facilities at St Dodimeads. A number of mourners were quite abusive after the service and if I had not found the funeral so moving I would of asked one or two to step into the vestry.

Ken's last wish was that his coffin should be carried by six Athletico players but I could not find a single one of the bastards who would do it for less than fifty quid. At least Trevor Proby had a reasonable excuse, he was decorating Pahdra Singh's house. (I wonder why Pahdra wanted an antique and bric-a-brac dealer to hang his wallpaper?) In the end, Lonsdale and Pugh's usual crew did the honours and old Pugh played 'You'll Never Walk Alone' on the organ. Even I shed a tear when the coffin was carried from the church to a recording of Jack Charlton's 'Geordie Sunday'.

Mrs Mentle and I both felt it was touching of Pugh to place a sticker in the back of the hearse which read 'Don't follow me, follow Athletico Whaddon.' She was also touched to think the club were going to display his ukelele in the trophy cabinet. I did not have the heart to tell her that Ken's beloved instrument was now a thousand tiny splinters after Trev Proby sat on it.

The service at the crematorium went off like a house on fire and on returning home I received a phone call from Pybus to say that, at a meeting of directors, Carter and Tilley had quit. It seems extraordinary that as manager I was not invited to attend, yet Reg, a mere team coach and raffle organiser, was.

As it was, I already knew of their resignation as both had phoned me to see if I would give them backing in a boardroom coup. They offered me considerable incentives to take up the role of figurehead in the new Whaddon regime; unlimited and free use of Tilley's taxis between 2.30 and 4.15 on Tuesday afternoons and generous discounts should I ever need the cat coiffured. However, I made my position very clear to the *Whaddon and Mitchley Argus* sports hack, Mark Crowe, when he came sniffing round at the funeral. 'Football to me,' I said, 'is about 22 fit men kicking a ball around a park, not about pot-bellied Freemasons passing the sherry decanter around a centrally heated Portakabin.' Even that buttock-licker Pybus seems worried that Pahdra Singh has replaced them with his shifty brothers but, as I told Crowe, having a property developer, an estate agent and a supermarket magnate on the board can only be good for the club.

My genius never fails to amaze. Four new players and Singh's miserly £53.23 safely deposited in my bank account, although he might ask for it back when he sees the crap I have signed. Old body disposer Pugh's nephew Duncan has been begging me for months to let him play and things have got so desperate I have no choice but to take him on. The fact that he is under-age could be a problem but a false beard, grey wig and strap-on paunch should be enough to fool any referee likely to officiate at an Athletico game. Mig Romerez did not even recognise a football when I showed him one but his exotic appearance should be enough to impress those bumpkins in 'The Tip' crowd. His pizza slices certainly rekindle memories of the good old days in football ... they taste like Dubbin. As for Wayne Pollock and Clive Smott, they are totally unknown quantities. In actual fact, I cannot even remember signing them! I must have bloody done so, because they both produced contracts and five or six witnesses who swore that, although I was completely paralytic, I signed them on last Monday night at the Duck and Forceps.

Pahdra Singh has just called to say that while he was at the funeral his house was burgled and a number of valuable antiques were stolen.

REMEMBER: TAKE CHESTER TO VET.

ATHLETICO -WHADDON

M/SV. DIVISION 3

TODAY ·V· FRAMPTON ROVERS

£1

* OFFICIAL PROGRAMME *

	P	W	D	L	PTS
CLANSFORD UTD	19	12	4	3	40
GOSLING CELTIC	19	10	5	4	35
NORTHTOWN	19	9	5	5	32
SCRIMLEY ARSENAL	19	8	5	6	29
ALBORNE	19	7	7	5	28
HELLINGBOROUGH	19	8	3	8	27
FRAMPTON ROVERS	19	7	5	7	26
REDLAND PARK AVENUE	19	6	7	6	25
TWITCHIT ALBION	19	7	4	8	25
LEECH TOWN	19	6	7	6	25
SPORTING HYDRA CHEMICALS	19	6	6	7	24
DORNING TOWN	18	6	6	6	24
CHAMDEN CITY RESERVES	19	6	5	8	23
FELTON	18	6	4	8	22
BOTHAM WDRS	19	6	3	10	21
SIDCOMBE	19	3	6	10	15
ATH. WHADDON	17	4	1	12	13

MANAGER'S NOTES

6th February '93

Once again, following our 1–0 defeat against Chamden City Reserves, the more bewildered of our supporters have subjected myself and other club officials to hysterical abuse and spit.

We ALL want the team to do well and, although results are going against us at present, I feel my policy of rebuilding will, in the long term, bring us success. There can be no instant cure. All right, the team are going through a temporary loss of form and that is not what you pay to see but, remember, football is a business not an entertainment. After saying that, I am sure every fan was heartened by the performance of our new quartet. The players, I know, especially enjoyed Miguel's tasty pizza slices at half-time.

*   *   *   *   *   *   *

Our leading goal-scorer, Royston Marley, is sadly on the move back to his native West Indies following receipt of special transfer forms. These forms are known as a Deportation Order. Unbeknownst to club officials, 'Royst' was in fact only a visitor to this country and his permit ran out two months ago. His departure will, of course, be a serious blow to our hopes of pulling away from the foot of the table. The return of 'Mad' Trevor 'Killer' Proby after another lengthy suspension should plug the gaping hole currently occupying our defence. Let us hope Trevor can surprise us all and stay on the park until the end of the season. It is through my perceptive ability to spot talent where others fail, that in signing Clive Smott, son of former manager Wally, I have found the perfect replacement for Royston Marley. Many of you, I know, believe

Smott's substitution after four minutes was because he was out of his depth, but I can assure you it is all part of my master plan which I am painstakingly developing on a game-by-game basis. I am more than a little confident that its fruition will be more than evident before the last kick of the season.

*   *   *   *   *   *   *

May I take this opportunity to dispel rumours, circulating among supporters, concerning Mr Pahdra Singh's involvement with an unnamed supermarket syndicate which is believed to be interested in purchasing 'The Tip' for redevelopment. Mr Singh has strongly denied these allegations in the Press and wishes to do so again. Unfortunately, fair-weather supporters tend to forget that no Athletico official gives less than 110 per cent to the club week in, Sundays off, and to think their heads could be turned in the hope of making financial personal gain is an insult.

CHAIRMAN'S CHAT

A jubilant Pahdra at a recent home game

Firstly, may I thank Mr Bence and the editors for allowing me a few lines in which to formally meet you all.

Although I have been a member of the board for less than a year, and chairman but a few weeks, I believe I have now been accepted into the bosom of the Athletico family. Were I to meet any of you at the golf club or the Mayor's banquet I am sure we could talk as equals over a glass of sherry and a snipe sandwich.

As the delegated head of this wonderful club, I see my duties as follows: firstly to my wife and children; secondly to other members of my family; then to consolidate my assets in any profitable manner I choose; and then to devote the rest of my time to the welfare of this club.

Though some of you may question my priorities we must be under no illusion. As that 'winger of wisdom' Leslie Bence has so often pointed out, football is a business. Luckily for Athletico, business is my business and something at which I excel, as many of you will know from the success of my 8-Day Superette in the High Street. Talking of which, this week Family Shopper Coffee Granules are only 64 pence a jar.

I know you see which side my fence is buttered, and if I can bring to football the organisational skills that have made me such a big fish in retailing, then Athletico Whaddon need have no fear of ending up on the slab.

But what of the criticism so often levelled at Leslie and myself that we have no idea how to run a football club? Well, my answer to this is simple. It was of no importance to the success of my Superette that I did not know how Spratts Processed Peas were manufactured, therefore when running a football team it can be of no importance if Leslie and I do not know how many players it contains.

As I have mentioned them, may I just point out that Spatts Peas are delicious with chipped potatoes or an omelette or simply naked from the tin. They are also four pence cheaper at my Superette than anywhere else in Whaddon.

As a businessman, it would be foolhardy of me to pour my own money nilly-willy into the club and so I am constantly on the look-out for companies willing to risk investing in a lowly but forward-looking team. We are grateful for the loose change of Messrs Lonsdale and Pugh, but let me assure you all, with a family-sized packet of Fisherman's Friend extra throat lozenges placed firmly on my heart, that I will strive in ever-decreasing circles to bring the sponsorship of a major international to 'The Tip' to provide much needed support to our glorious team.

All I ask is that you are patient. Leslie Bence is a man with the gift of impaired vision, a vision that will take time to grow and expand. If you have forgotten this article within the next hour remember, please, just two things. Firstly, that as chairman of Athletico Whaddon I will never devote less than 36 per cent of my time to the club and, secondly, there are, this season, substantial discounts to any supporter spending over £20 at my Superette. Happy football and happy shopping.

PAHDRA

ATHLETICO WHADDON – THE GREAT GAMES

Les Bence looks at some of the great matches he has witnessed.

September 1992
CHAMDEN CITY RESERVES 1, ATHLETICO WHADDON 2

When I suggested this feature for the programme in the club-house, I was amazed no one put forward a match from my period as manager. Therefore to kick off this irregular feature I have chosen one myself – as it happens, the first game of this season.

Was it only five months ago we were all talking of promotion as a certainty? In my position you soon learn that football has only one certainty, that at the end of ninety minutes the final whistle blows unless there is extra time.

As you will recall, I have persistently warned you all about taking promotion for granted and I am sure if you read back over my programme notes you will find I have not once alluded to it. Having said that, the vague possibility that we may end this season by finishing bottom and going out of the League remains incomprehensible to me and I am at a loss to explain it.

How different it all seemed back in September, though. A new season, a new League and a great bit of luck. Chamden City Reserves could only find five players. From July onwards the town of Whaddon had waited with bated breath. Expectation had been rampant throughout June but, come the pre-season friendlies of August, football fever had reached dizzy heights. Those warm-up games had given no indication of the glory to come.

Expectation was boiling when we all climbed into Reg's minibus and headed for Chamden on that balmy September Saturday. Behind us, the fanatical 'Whaddon Army' piled into the social club's Morris Minor and the black-and-yellow horde sped along the Mitchley by-pass before crashing into the back of us when Reg's brakes failed. With only twenty minutes to go before kick-off we crawled into the Willowmead Stadium, our confidence uncomfortably perched on the gear stick.

Every general has his own method for preparing his troops for battle and I am no exception. No relaxing by the pool or light lunch over *Football Focus* for my lads. No, I tend to break into a crate of Nettles Old Fester.

It was only minutes before the Athletico gladiators took to the field that Chamden's assistant manager, Frank Spanner, announced that owing to an outbreak of foot and mouth amongst the first team, they had been forced to include six second-team men in their squad at Billington Euphonia. This left only five players to face us. Despite pleas from both Spanner and the referee I insisted that the match go ahead, pointing out that not only a principle but also three certain points were at stake.

Before a morose crowd limply reaching double figures battle commenced at three o'clock. With regular centre-forward Kelvin Simple taking over duties in goal, the City Reserves had only four players left on the park. They noted with fear Terry Wade's eight goals within a minute and it was lucky for them the referee had not kicked off before he scored them. Taking my place on the touchline, I noticed as we kicked off the reassuring sight of Ken Mentle in the grandstand giving me the thumbs up before disappearing through his tip-up seat.

As soon as 'Jock' McDougall sent a blistering back pass

crashing against his own crossbar in the first minute, I knew there were only two teams in it. Chamden performed like men possessed and even had the audacity to mount wave after wave of attacks. An uncharacteristic hard tackle by Darren Twink sent a Chamden defender writhing in agony and my hopes soared in expectation of their side being further depleted. 'Twinky', however, without question the fairest and most sporting player ever to don an Athletico shirt, was full of remorse and insisted that the referee, who had not even blown for a foul, send him off. Running on to the pitch I attempted to dissuade Twink, but he remained distraught and adamant. Seeing that no serious injury had been done to the Chamden player, Darren settled on grabbing the referee's notebook and booking himself.

As half-time approached and with the score at 0–0, Reg and I shuffled nervously on the bench, but the duck was about to be broken. Chamden full-back, Vernon Maradonna, intercepted a pass between Doyle and Proby and, with the rest of the Athletico defence sharing a cigarette on the touch-line, and John Slack reading *War and Peace* behind his goal, slotted the ball home to give the Reserves a half-time lead.

I entered the dressing room like Atilla entered Rome, by flushing all the oranges down the lavatory. The situation called for some drastic action and so I laid it on the line; either they won this game or I would resign. It was not until the cheers had subsided and Reg Pybus had pointed out the rashness of my statement that I decided instead on getting the match abandoned. Confronting the referee over his mug of vodka, I insisted that he call the game off as it was obvious the five Chamden lads were at a complete disadvantage against our full team. He, however, disagreed and despite my threat to take the matter to the County FA, Lancaster Gate and Esther Rantzen, he decided to carry on.

I then produced a master stroke. I suppose it was just my managerial instinct coming to the fore, but I decided to make a tactical substitution. I pulled off my entire six-man defence and, much to his surprise, sent on Reg Pybus as the lone forward and moved the forwards back into defence.

No sooner had I retaken my touchline seat than Reg, a mile off-side and with the referee unsighted, had hammered home the equaliser. Unfortunately, leaping from my seat in the dug-out, I cracked my skull on its roof and the world turned black.

I eventually came round in the Chamden General Hospital and on the slab next to me was club chairman, Ken Mentle, an oxygen pump beside him, a nurse frantically thumping his chest and Ken rambling deliriously about a Micky Deere scorcher from the penalty spot which had given us victory.

The only sad note was that I missed the second half and was given no credit for our victory, despite masterminding the whole tactical approach to the game. As I told the *Whaddon and Mitchley Argus* and the 'Sporting Mauve', the game went precisely to plan, yet they claimed we were totally outplayed and only secured victory because by the last quarter the 'five Chamden heroes' were completely knackered.

LES IN CONFIDENCE

WEDNESDAY, 3rd FEBRUARY

A knock at the door this morning turned out to be a
young girl in floods of tears, asking for me. At first I
thought it was something to do with Chester, you hear
so many disgusting stories about Tech. colleges these
days, but then I realised that he would not be interested
in a girl unless she had cantilever overhangs and could
be seen five miles away from the top of a bus. As it
turned out she was Royston Marley's girlfriend, who
told me he had been taken away by the police and was
being deported. His last words, she said, as he was
driven away, were for me. He wanted to thank me for
having such an undying belief in his footballing ability
and for working tirelessly to further his career in
soccer. She told me that he just had time to wrap a
small gift of appreciation. In a flood of tears, some my
own, she presented me with four frozen chicken por-
tions.

Brilliant! How many ruddy goals am I going to get
from a frozzled chicken bit! Actually, a damn sight more
than from that stiff gherkin Smott. Hells bells, I should
never have quit abstinence. If this is the sort of crap I
sign when I am canned I really must try and get back
on the wagon.

Watching Smotty's four-minute debut – missing an
open goal whilst tying his bootlace, refusing to take a
second-minute penalty until he had washed his shin
pads in the puddle on the centre circle, then when he
did take it hitting the corner flag – I could feel the
supporters forcing my head further and further down
on the block. I don't know which was more humiliating,

that git's performance, or the ape-like dance and inane grinning of Reg Pybus when I pulled him off.

My other 'new boys' were just as dire. Romerez was pathetic and his interpretation of the new 'no passing back to the goalkeeper' rule was bloody unique. I have never seen a player catch a football in his mouth and spit it back to his keeper before. Still, he didn't have to spoil his debut by insisting he left the game ten minutes before the interval so he could prepare his half-time pizza slices.

I did not dare risk Pollock and young Duncan Pugh and so I left them firmly on the bench. Even that did not stop Pugh getting quizzical looks from the referee who asked about his age, so I told him that he was not the Pugh named as sub in the programme but the club mascot.

As results get worse, I still manage to bluff the board into believing I have a long-term strategy that will see us pulling away from the bottom within weeks. I don't have a plan, all I have is a well thumbed copy of *The Alex Ferguson Book of Footballing Euphemisms*.

Rumours continue in the supporters' club, and the Trevor Howard Theme Bar of the Duck and Forceps, that the Singh brothers have earmarked 'The Tip' for re-development. Personally I think it is a load of rubbish. Who would want to build on that bog? As I told a couple of surveyors I met at the ground earlier today, 'Building on here would be like trying to wallpaper a Slumberland mattress.'

ATHLETICO -WHADDON

M/SV. DIVISION 3

TODAY

·V·

SPORTING HYDRA CHEMICALS

£1

✱ OFFICIAL PROGRAMME ✱

	P	W	D	L	PTS
CLANSFORD UTD	20	13	4	3	43
GOSLING CELTIC	20	11	5	4	38
NORTHTOWN	20	9	5	6	32
SCRIMLEY ARSENAL	20	9	5	6	32
ALBORNE	20	8	7	5	31
FRAMPTON ROVERS	20	8	5	7	29
REDLAND PARK AVENUE	20	7	7	6	28
HELLINGBOROUGH	20	8	3	9	27
SPORTING HYDRA CHEMICALS	20	7	6	7	27
TWITCHIT ALBION	20	7	4	9	25
DORNING TOWN	19	6	7	6	25
LEECH TOWN	20	6	7	7	25
CHAMDEN CITY RESERVES	20	6	6	8	24
FELTON	19	6	4	9	22
BOTHAM WDRS	20	6	3	11	21
SIDCOMBE	20	4	6	10	18
ATH. WHADDON	18	4	1	13	13

MANAGER'S NOTES

20th February '93

During half-time today a number of police officers will be questioning you all over the disappearance, during the early hours of Monday morning, of our grandstand.

The 'Bog Hole', as we affectionately knew it, recently renamed the Ken Mentle Memorial Stand, mysteriously vanished overnight and its whereabouts are still unknown. Besides being the only decent covered area at 'The Tip', the stand was a local landmark, and although not in the same class perhaps as the Eiffel Tower, it was held in great affection by nearby residents. The effort involved in removing it is totally out of proportion with the financial gain anyone could hope to recoup from its sale as scrap metal and firewood. There is no logical explanation for the theft. GIVE OUR STAND BACK.

Have you seen our stand? Keep 'em peeled

On the field a fortnight ago we unfortunately caught Frampton Rovers on a good day as they ran out 5–1 victors. However, it was encouraging to see Wayne Pollock get on the score sheet in his debut match with a goal off the back of his head as he stood watching a flock of swans fly overhead. Also encouraging was the performance of Trevor Proby in failing to get his name taken or sent off. This is all the more remarkable as he was responsible for giving away all five penalties. WELL DONE, TREV!

*   *   *   *   *   *   *

Once again I have attracted the wrath of many supporters who think they know more about football than the eleven 'Stiffs' they profess to follow. This may well be so, but I get very tired when they attempt to banter tactics with me.

My appointment as team manager was a radical move on the board's part and my policies must reflect their cavalier approach. Many people were outraged when I lined up a side with ten forwards in our cup game with Hatton Matadors, but remember we came back from 7–0 down. True, we still lost, 7–2, but that is what experimentation is all about.

Football is all about outwitting your opponents, never playing to a formula and always having a change of underwear. It is only through my imaginative shuffling of the aces that we are able to stay ahead of the pack. In the words of John Motson, 'No footballer is an island.' Well, no manager is an isthmus.

*   *   *   *   *   *   *

Those of you who are still concerned about our results should take comfort in the fact that these are early days and with the season barely three-quarters over we still have ten games remaining in which to pull away from the bottom. Should the unthinkable occur, a bottom three position, it should be remembered that we cannot be relegated from the Third Division. As there is no Fourth Division, it would mean playing ourselves every week.

YOUR LINE TO LES

Dear Mr Bence,

So you want me to be constructive, eh, Les? Well, all right.

Look, in my day, before the war, we always had wingers, none of this booting up the middle and hoping for the best. If we had some wingers, Les, I tell you we'd create havoc with our crosses.

Noughts mean 0, crosses mean goals, that's how I see it.

Back in my day we often used to have five or six wingers on the field at once. Course, the ball never left the centre spot because they were all hugging the touchline and refused to get it, but you ask any of the 'old timers' and they will tell you straight, Les, bring back the wingers!

No offence,

G.P.

Dear G.P.,

Thank you for your suggestion. Kicking the ball up field and 'hoping for the best', as you put it, is fundamental to my strategy this season and a change in policy now would only disrupt the well-oiled machine I have created.

The winger belongs to football's more flamboyant age, when players were given free rein on the field and the managers' instructions were nothing more than, 'Get out there and earn your ten bob.' Today a player is simply a pawn, part of a highly organised unit working to a manager's pre-determined set of tactics. In our case, this is kick and rush.

Today, primitive skill on the field has been replaced by brains on the bench and, as such, football is now on an intellectual par with chess and skittles.

No offence,

Les.

Bency,

Until we discovered your football club, Saturday afternoons for me and my mates meant spraying rude words on the side of the Co-op or hijacking shopping trolleys.

'The Tip' has given a new meaning to the weekend. No doubt you have spotted the 'Proby Pack', as we call ourselves, clustered at the Sewage Lane end, our shaven heads painted with such menacing slogans as 'Cut out the long balls' or, on a couple of big heads, 'Using two sweepers is a tactical error, Les'.

The thing is, boss, we still think something is missing at the club. Where's the aggro? Nobody wants to fight and the police only make arrests if we telephone them ourselves to report trouble. Every club worth its salt has a hooligan element, so what has happened to ours?

Steve 'The Razor'

Dear Razor,

I cannot condone violence outside of the Oliver Reed Cellar Bar at the Duck and Forceps, certainly not here at 'The Tip' where we pride ourselves on our family atmosphere.

Les

Dear Mr Manager,

I am a young lad of eighteen who has been approached by your official, Mr Reg Pybus, with an invitation to join your club as a player. Although I say so myself, I am not without skill, having represented the county at schoolboy level. I would certainly jump at the chance of a career in football.

There is, however, a problem. I do not drink. Friends tell me that this could seriously hamper my chances of joining Athletico, as it is rumoured your club is just an excuse for getting smashed four or five times a week. Please advise.

Yours,
K.T.

Dear K.T.,
How refreshing to hear of a young lad whose only vice is to want a career in football. Unfortunately, socialising is a vital ingredient when one is a member of a team. Remember, in non-League football a player is respected not only for the number of goals he can put away.

L. Bence

Dear Mr Bence,
Your introduction of a letters page to the match programme should be congratulated. I think it was very brave of you, especially as supporters will use it as an opportunity to criticise you and the team publicly.

However, although your replies are often thoughtful and considered, I have detected a worrying trend of late. Like some of your more illustrious colleagues (Ron Atkinson, Graham Taylor, etc.), you have a tendency to say a lot but to say nothing at the same time. Please remember, Mr Bence, that the majority of Athletico supporters are plain ordinary countryfolk, and to us, words and phrases such as 'perspicacious' and 'total player interface' have no meaning at all.

I am convinced that simple answers, in working man's English and full of hard facts (often lacking in your replies), would alleviate the impression many of us hold that you have become a master in the art of waffling.

What we want is down-to-earth accountability, not lots of incomprehensible grand ideas. Sorry about this, Mr Bence, but do you not agree that sometimes your answers are just too vague?

Yours sincerely,
A. J. Vine

Dear Mr Vine,
Possibly.

Cheers,
Les.

Dear Les,
What do you think our chances are in Europe next season?

The England boss is too much of a diplomat and never gives a clue to his plans, but I am sure a no-nonsense chap like you will not fudge the issue.

Yours in anticipation,
J.M.

Dear J.M.,
I have not followed international football for well over twenty years, preferring to concentrate on the bread and butter of non-League soccer, so I have no idea what Alf Ramsey thinks. I can say with confidence, however, that he knows nothing about Athletico Whaddon. Frankly, we would have a mountain to climb to get 'The Stiffs' into Europe, but you never know. If I can build the squad the way I wish and not be forced to part with exceptional talent like Colin Webley, then anything is possible. I am sorry my reply is so brief, but having just cut my thumb I am unable to continue writing.

Yours in antiseptic,
Les Bence

Dear Les,
As you know I am married to Dave Doyle, right back with the club. I am, I think you will agree, 25 years old with a vivacious personality and one hell of a figure. As you have often told me, Leslie, as a wife of a current first-team member, it is my duty to flaunt these qualities whenever possible, for the good of the club. So may I ask you, Leslie, yourself blessed

with endless charisma and, may I say, sex appeal, where am I going wrong on the terraces?

Neither slinky dresses nor thigh-throttling jeans and undulating cleavage seem to arouse the slightest passion into those zombies on the terraces. This does nothing for my ego. Can you offer any explanation?

Yours in confidence,
(Name and address supplied)

Dear Zara Doyle,
Believe me, your appearance is noted every home game, especially by your husband, a consequence of which is that his game is suffering. How much more satisfying for your ego if you were to flaunt your assets around C&A on a Saturday afternoon.

I can only suppose the fans ignore you because they are too engrossed in my thought-provoking programme notes.

Yours in hope,
L.B.

SUPPORTERS' CLUB NEWS

Dave Bull, who many of you will know as a fanatical 'Stiff' and athlete in his own right, has been banned from carrying on shot-putt practice in the bar. Last Friday's unfortunate accident left the club with no alternative.

A framed photograph of Jimmy Hill was dislodged behind the bar and fell, shattering bottles and glasses. Barman Mike Wheeler slipped whilst attempting to catch the picture, badly slashing his wrist on the broken glass and at the same time dropping his lighted cigarette into a box of Buxtons Tripe and Strawberry Flavoured Crisps. These then ignited and the flames caught the draperies behind alight.

In an attempt to extinguish the flames, a number of youths broke into the Space Invaders machine, filled their pockets with an estimated £140 worth of ten pence pieces and hurtled the machine at the blaze. Sadly, it failed to smother the flames but travelled on through the window, coming to rest on Mr Singh's Bentley, causing an estimated £567 worth of damage.

Three cheers, then, for club steward, Rolly Hill. Rolly single-handedly attempted to apprehend the youths, put out the fire and administer first aid to barman Wheeler. Luckily the carbon dioxide stopped the bleeding, 1,400 coins smothered the blaze and the three youths were detained by five yards of sticking plaster and a lead poultice.

The aftermath of these events is that the supporters' club now has debts totalling £4,684. Thanks, Dave.

*   *   *   *   *   *   *

This Sunday we will be holding our popular 'Question of Soccer' quiz in the bar. This week Les Bence and two of his squad will take on a team of religious fundamentalists from the local mosque. During the interval no questions will be asked.

*   *   *   *   *   *   *

'Going Down, Staying Up, Going Down' is the first Athletico Whaddon fanzine. It has been put together by a group of younger supporters, and the first issue comes complete with a free disabled driver sticker which should make parking at away games much easier. The magazine costs 20 pence and supply your own staples.

LES IN CONFIDENCE

THURSDAY, 18th FEBRUARY

The mental strain of football management is phenomenal. What I do not need is to be awoken at 4 a.m. in the depths of winter, forced from my bed and summoned to gawp at an empty space where once a football stand stood.

Since its 'theft' my living room has been under siege from Mark 'The Scoop' Crowe, the *Argus* sports hack. Already Steve Gillery and myself have suffered the humiliation of having to feign tears, whilst pointing at nothing, for the sake of press photographers.

This morning, as I cooked Crowe breakfast, he told me the story had 'national' written all over it. He told me he would be phoning in copy to the *Sun* although, having no sex angle, they might not be interested. I pointed out that the ground was once part of Tip Farm and that on rainy days Bob Crudge still used it for artificial insemination. Therefore, technically somebody had stolen a fertility clinic.

It was decided at the last cash crisis meeting to get rid of the grandstand and claim the insurance, only local radio jockey, Keith Labone, thought there might be some insurance fiddle on the go. Pahdra Singh handled his on-air interview brilliantly, and pointed out to Labone that grandstands are not insured against theft. What that smarmy jock did not know was that a cousin of Proby, who is in insurance, had insured the grandstand disguised as a car – third party fire and theft. I am not sorry to see the stand go because being shabby, leaky at the back, and all but condemned, it was a constant reminder of the team's own position. At lunchtime I called in the Duck and Forceps for pie and chips in the Nanette Newman Brasserie. This was the first time I had dared to show my face in the D and F since our 7–2 drubbing in the Cup. The team have only themselves to blame. Three minutes before kick-off is not the time to stage a dressing room revolt. As usual I had not named my squad so as to keep the opposition guessing — all I had announced was that there would be eleven players in the team. The 'uprising' came from the forwards who moaned that they never had anything to do. I made a few suggestions, creating chances, scoring goals, but it did not get through. In fact, they flatly refused to play unless they could take over in defence. Well, there was nothing for it, I had to lay down the law in no uncertain terms. Luckily the timely intervention of Trevor Proby's left boot into my right ear quickened everyone's resolve to reach a compromise. Reluctantly I agreed that goalie John Slack should have a ten-man defence in front of him. However, as I had promised attacking football, I named them all as forwards.

Optimism is my middle name because, unable to agree on a name, my parents stuck a pin in a dictionary. But optimistic is also my nature and, although the end of season is in sight, I still believe a final League position of second from bottom is obtainable. At least I will not have to suffer relegation again because the Multivite Vegeburger/Singletons Valve Replacement League Division III is the pits.

Threatening phone bills are quite common in this house, but in the last few days abusive calls have become popular, with an unknown voice offering to dismember certain of my vital organs unless I quit the manager's job. My suspicion first fell on Reg Pybus, but I am now certain it is Howard Wilkinson, seeking some

116

perverted pleasure to compensate for his monumental gaff in signing that prat Colin Webley.

ATHLETICO WHADDON

M/SV. DIVISION 3.

TODAY · V · NORTHTOWN

£1

✱ OFFICIAL PROGRAMME ✱

	P	W	D	L	PTS
CLANSFORD UTD	21	13	4	4	43
GOSLING CELTIC	21	12	5	4	41
NORTHTOWN	21	10	5	6	35
ALBORNE	21	9	7	5	34
SCRIMLEY ARSENAL	21	9	6	6	33
FRAMPTON ROVERS	21	8	6	7	30
REDLAND PARK AVENUE	21	7	8	6	29
TWITCHIT ALBION	21	8	4	9	28
HELLINGBOROUGH	21	8	4	9	28
SPORTING HYDRA CHEMICALS	21	7	7	7	28
DORNING TOWN	20	6	7	7	25
LEECH TOWN	21	6	7	8	25
FELTON	20	7	4	9	25
CHAMDEN CITY RESERVES	21	6	7	8	25
BOTHAM WDRS	21	6	3	12	21
SIDCOMBE	21	4	7	10	19
ATH. WHADDON	19	4	1	14	13

MANAGER'S NOTES

27th February '93

Incompetence has, I fear, reached epidemic proportions of late in our local police force. I can only assume this is the reason they have failed to make any progress in hunting down our missing grandstand. I have myself spent many hours at the police station compiling an accurate photo-fit of the stand and, through my many contacts in the local underworld, supplied them with the names of many undesirables known to deal in second-hand wood.

Despite this assistance, they insist on concentrating their enquiries around Trevor Proby's new 'rustic' conservatory. In my opinion, they should stop hounding law-abiding citizens and set about catching the obvious culprits, whoever they are.

*   *   *   *   *   *   *

Following my success in transferring Colin Webley to Leeds United, other top clubs are now casting their chequebooks towards the talent I have nurtured here at Athletico. Only the other week, Reg Pybus spotted the chief scout for Scunthorpe United in the crowd. Obviously he did not make himself known so we can only speculate as to who he was watching, but we are all hoping that Trevor Proby will soon get the call.

Likewise, supporters have reported to me that a well known, flamboyant Football League Premier Division chairman has been seen at 'The Tip'. We may assume that he is not spying on players and so must be on the lookout for managerial talent. Should the call come within the next week, I shall be taking out a full-page advert in the *Whaddon and Mitchley Argus* to express my thanks to you all for your support during my short period as manager.

*   *   *   *   *   *   *

It must be a rare sight, even in this division, for spectators to see the home side knock in eleven goals in one match, but that is what the Alborne supporters witnessed last Tuesday night. It seems ridiculous for me to try and offer excuses why we were so comprehensively beaten, but the fact that we were well below full strength certainly gave Alborne a ten-goal advantage. Romerez, McDougall and Smith all had work commitments, whilst Jason Pratt and Darren Twink were fulfilling their community service orders. With only ten men available I had no choice but to let Clive Smott play the whole ninety minutes, and even club coach and near octogenarian, Reg Pybus, was forced to get out his old boots and wicker shorts.

*   *   *   *   *   *   *

Today we take on Northtown, who beat us 4–2 back in October, thus denting our then red-hot title hopes. Today's game is sure to be a needle match and, with the runners-up spot a distinct possibility for Northtown, the 'Sausage Men' will have a formidable task in trying to take three points from our rock-solid defence.

*   *   *   *   *   *   *

In an effort to boost club funds, a small tent will soon be found on the far side of the ground. This is to be the new club shop where we hope to sell T-shirts, calendars and fluffy bookmarks in the club's colours.

WHAT THE WIVES SAY...

An intimate insight into the lives of Athletico's stars. As told by the ladies who know them best . . . !

TRACY DEERE

My Micky is just a normal human being at home. I know a lot of fans will find that hard to believe. They also think he must be dominant, decisive and virile but he's not, he's just as he is on the field. He has few hobbies outside of football although, even with his eyesight, he does like reading sell-by dates on goods in shops.

CARMEN ROMEREZ

El Bence, I tell you straight. Back home in Barçelona Miguel could not care less about football. The business always come first. People say he only joined your team by mistake because he loves dancing. He asked a customer if there was a flamenco class in Whaddon, he said there was no:, but there were twelve ballerinas at 'The Tip'. Miguel, he just loves to dance, he try anything.

TINA MEEK

Phil likes to spend all his free time with our two boys, Reg and Ronnie. They are out most nights visiting a post office somewhere or repossessing cars. But Phil will never miss his football, not even if he has to lie low for a couple of months. I think he goes training because he knows the police can never find an Athletico training session.

He gets so excited on match days he is often up and about by noon. If it is a home match, though, he will usually get up around two-thirty. I tell you there ain't nothing he would not do for that football club. Once he went up to London with Trevor Proby and a crowbar to sort out that Des Lynam geezer.

ALISON McDOUGALL

Most players' wives at Whaddon are like their husbands and could not care less about football, but both Jock and I live and breathe Athletico. I like to 'shoot' every Whaddon game and it is nothing for Jock to spend a whole weekend analysing, in minute detail, every little aspect of his instruction manual in the hope he can learn to operate the video machine.

Because his heart is devoted to the club, it does not mean his attitude and commitment are always on a par with yours, Les. Luckily, I am there to make sure he snaps out of it. When mid-table apathy sets in, I force him to undertake a rigorous training session which I, naturally, oversee. His programme includes hourly cold showers, a diet of raw cabbage and, on match days, he is suspended from the balcony by his feet, whilst I beat some sense into him with a copy of the 'Sporting Mauve'.

CINDY POLLOCK

Even now I can't get used to my Wayne being a famous footballer. I'll never forget when he came home one night a few months ago and said he'd met this old man who could tell fortunes by reading the dregs in the bottom of a beer glass. Well, Wayne is very gullible when he's had a few and when you, Leslie, told him he was going to be a football star, it went to his head and he happily paid you the £10 signing-on fee.

He seems to be enjoying it, but he has a weak chest and really he shouldn't be out on cold winter afternoons. I must say, though, I think it is very good of you, Les, to let him play those frosty games between November and April in his overcoat.

VAL WADE
Don't talk to me about Terry, Les.

SPOTLIGHT ON THE GREAT PLAYERS

BILL DODD (1932–36)

Bill Dodd, club captain in the 1930s, was one of those players who always gave his all for ninety minutes.

Those ninety minutes he played over three seasons had a lingering influence on fellow players and league positions alike. Bill, who rarely played more than five minutes in any game because of a heart condition, was one of that rare breed who made the art of football look deceptively simple.

When he was on the field, chairs were placed at regular intervals along each touchline so that when he made a break on the wing, he had plenty of opportunity to rest before continuing his blistering run.

KEN MENTLE (1936–40)

Younger supporters will remember the late, lamented Ken as our dedicated chairman for over forty years, but as a player he was perhaps the most talented the club has ever produced. Many believe he should have had a career in professional soccer but in those days, as now, top scouts were unaccountably remiss in visiting 'The Tip'. Perhaps Ken's one failing was that he belonged to a breed of footballer who would later include Charlie George, Rodney Marsh and Emlyn Hughes – big heads.

As a captain, Ken, often resembling an unfit Oswald Mosley, would blatantly push his fellow team mates off the ball if they were in a goal-scoring position, and take the glory for himself. In recounting his goal-scoring triumphs, Ken

Mentle had the unique ability to empty the Duck and Forceps in six minutes flat.

John Motson once said 'This man is like a little human dynamo. He may only be 5 ft 4 ins but he is a giant among small players.' He could have been talking about Ken Mentle. Actually, it was Francis Lee.

BERT FUDGE (1936–40)

The legendary Bert Fudge

That great side of the late 1930s, always remembered as 'Mentle's Mediocres', had so many forgotten players that uncovering Bert Fudge ranks as a milestone in twentieth-century archeology.

When it came to football Bert had one thing on his mind, pigeons. Easily distinguishable in his bird-lime-encrusted shirt and shorts, he often had a look in his eye that spoke of clouds and freedom, rather than the shin-splitting hordes bearing down on him in the shape of the Corton Heath Corinthians. During a crucial match v. Royal Artillery Reserves, his flock of pigeons landed on the goal-line, robbing Whaddon of a last-minute winner. Four birds died in the knowledge that they had pulled off one of the best saves ever seen at 'The Tip'.

ROYSTON MARLEY (1992)

If proof were ever needed that I had a gift for spotting talent then my signing of Royston Marley was it.

Sadly, the intricacies of immigration laws and of jealousy at Lancaster Gate means Marley is no longer available to us. Despite his role as a vital link in my wheel, during his short stay with us I worked tirelessly to further his career. Indeed, I informed both Stoke City and Tring United that they were interested in him. However, with a customary lack of vision, Stoke did not even bother to reply.

Royston was one of the best players we have had since the 1930s. Trevor Proby is another, of course, but his notables should not be discussed in polite company.

LES IN CONFIDENCE

WEDNESDAY, 24th FEBRUARY
ASH WEDNESDAY

The grandstand/insurance fiddle has been a complete balls up. Pahdra Singh has told me that although Proby's cousin did manage to register the stand as a car, he did so describing it as a 1964 Skoda with 300,000 miles on the clock. Instead of the eight grand pay-out we had all expected, what we got was seventy quid and nowhere to shelter from the rain.

I have my fingers crossed, but my own finances may be on the up. There seems every possibility that Trev Proby will be sent down in the near future. I must admit, I credited Proby with a bit more sense. Who in their right mind would build a conservatory with Athletico Whaddon FC emblazoned along the side, and have window frames made from wood bearing the words 'Seats 1–10' and 'Ticket holders only'?

No less than three supporters, all before opening time, have told me that they know for certain that a League chairman has been watching me in recent weeks. I have just put together a mail shot which I am sending to all Premier League chairmen. It includes my CV, a forged testimonial from Mike Channon and the offer to work my first season for a ridiculous 70K a year.

Chester so churned my stomach at breakfast this morning I could not face my sausage, egg and Guinness. The reason for such severe indigestion was a deplorable rag called 'Going Down, Staying Up, Going Down'. This, he gleefully informed me, was the official mouthpiece of the fans where supporters took delight in telling management and directors where to get off. To me it looked like four sheets of Kleenex wiped in something unspeakable and stapled as far away from the fold as possible. It said little about the state of football at Athletico, but quite a lot about the lefty, New Age lecturers who encourage students at the Tech. to run up this garbage.

Naturally, in football management you expect ridicule and criticism, and you must always rise above it, especially if it is constructive, but this poor excuse for a handkerchief seems obsessed not with football but with my receding hairline, e.g. the 'Spot The Baldy' competition on page two, and with making juvenile remarks about my beer gut. Football criticism of any kind is meagre (p6–32), and their undying praise for Reg Pybus' five minutes against Alborne is laughable if not libellous. To say I forcibly removed him in a head-lock because he was 'In five short minutes, playing himself back into the job of Athletico manager', is not only true but also likely to get this fanzine banned within a fifteen-mile radius of 'The Tip'.

'Jock' McDougall called round with the merchandise for the club shop. Violence, even after a bucketful of wallop, is not in my nature but, after seeing the goods, throats were throttled. Who is going to buy a T-shirt with the words 'Athletico Whaddon' felt-tipped on to a piece of paper, and Blu-tac'd over an Iron Maiden logo? Is it any wonder McDougall is now on loan to Mitchley Infirmary?

ATHLETICO WHADDON

M/SV. DIVISION 3.

TODAY

· V ·

CLANSFORD UNITED

£1

✳ OFFICIAL PROGRAMME ✳

	P	W	D	L	PTS
GOSLING CELTIC	23	14	5	4	47
CLANSFORD UTD	23	13	4	6	43
ALBORNE	23	11	7	5	40
NORTHTOWN	23	11	6	6	39
SCRIMLEY ARSENAL	23	9	8	6	35
REDLAND PARK AVENUE	23	8	9	6	33
HELLINGBOROUGH	23	9	5	9	32
SPORTING HYDRA CHEMICALS	23	8	8	7	32
FRAMPTON ROVERS	23	8	7	8	31
FELTON	22	9	4	9	31
TWITCHIT ALBION	23	9	4	10	31
CHAMDEN CITY RESERVES	23	6	9	8	27
DORNING TOWN	22	6	7	9	25
LEECH TOWN	23	6	7	10	25
SIDCOMBE	23	5	8	10	23
BOTHAM WDRS	23	6	3	14	21
ATH. WHADDON	21	4	2	15	14

MANAGER'S NOTES

6th March '93

Well, I hope all those supporters who complained about lack of entertainment and commitment witnessed our last home game with Northtown.

We were 2–0 up at half-time, through two goals by Dave Doyle, and the change round was barely three minutes old when Ubahni Singh, signed seconds before kick-off, netted his first goal for the club. As if this were not enough, the last quarter saw some of the most exciting football I have ever witnessed and certainly vindicated the raising of admission prices by 68 per cent. Down to nine men, our lads deserve the highest praise for a 3–3 draw.

Once again, though, Trevor Proby received his marching orders and I fear we may never see him in a 'Stiffs' shirt again. The club now have no option but to dispense with his services.

I usually have some sympathy for a player who is dismissed simply for being over-aggressive, but I draw the line when this aggro is carried out on a fellow team mate. The deliberate breaking of goalkeeper John Slack's arm by Proby, putting Slack out for the rest of the season, may well sound the death knell for Division Three football at 'The Tip'. Today, all-round utility player, Clive Smott, will wear the keepers' shorts even though Slack is two sizes bigger.

*　　　*　　　*　　　*　　　*　　　*　　　*

Once again my keen eye for spotting talent, where others see only incompetence, has sparkled in bringing Ubahni Singh to the club. A distant nephew of our chairman, 'Hani' is the most exciting prospect I have seen this week. In fact, so impressed am I with his performance that I shall personally be paying his train fare from Birmingham twice a week.

*   *   *   *   *   *   *

As one new face appears another departs. During our game with Sporting Hydra Chemicals in which we trounced them before going down 1–0, Duncan Pugh's false beard came off in a goal-mouth fracas and he was questioned, at length, by referee Bobby Maxwell. The upshot is a fine of £543 for playing an ineligible and non-registered player, and a tearful farewell for Duncan.

*   *   *   *   *   *   *

Finally, may I dispell a couple of nonsensical rumours that are currently circulating. Fans have besieged me of late claiming that in my last programme notes I announced the opening of a club shop. Having read through my notes with a fine toothpick, I can find no mention of the tent on the far side of the ground whatsoever.

News that Mr Pahdra Singh has become an executive with Singh Development Corporation has also started tongues wagging again over the future of 'The Tip'. Let me make it quite clear, Pahdra Singh is committed to this club 116 per cent. To think he would let it fold for the sake of enormous personal gain is, quite frankly, ludicrous. Any fears you may have are, believe me, like Maidstone United, completely groundless.

YOUR LINE TO LES

Ted Cox is almost unique among Athletico supporters as he is one of only a handful who voluntarily attend away games. His presence is much appreciated by the team, and the sight of his moped chained to the grandstand always boosts the team's morale. Below you will find a match report for our thrilling 11–0 defeat at Alborne the other week, which Ted included in a recent letter.

With the 'Stiffs' only able to field ten men, including Reg Pybus, this was always going to be a tough game.

Keith Simmons, Alborne's lethal striker, put them ahead with a goal from the centre spot right on kick-off, and it was immediately obvious that our radical 0–2–7 formation was not going to work. Within another two minutes Simmons was two-thirds towards completing his hat trick after he outpaced all six defenders and side-footed the ball past goalkeeper Slack, who had been caught unawares as at the time he was trying to impress a group of young girls in the crowd by swinging on the crossbar. Undaunted, Athletico played as one man. That man was Reg Pybus. Reg looked at least three divisions better than anyone else on the park, and many of us thought it incomprehensible of 'Bencey' to literally drag him off after only five minutes. In a perverse way, losing their best player lifted the 'Stiffs' and they came more into the game, although Micky Deere and Terry Wade were both booked for negative play. However, failing to operate a successful offside trap, the Whaddon defence saw Combes walk in goal number three.

Simmons dispossessed Meek from the restart and, as he did with his first goal, secured his hat trick by scoring from the centre spot. On the stroke of half-time, Alborne's one-legged defender, Brown, successfully dummied the entire Whaddon back row to give Alborne a 5–0 lead at the interval.

Despite the valiant cries of 'We are the Bencey Boys' from the faithful few, we were subjected to jeers from the Alborne crowd as fighting broke out between the Athletico players on their way back to the dressing room. Order was only restored when manager Bence dowsed them in a bucket of cold Bovril.

The second half began with some of the most remarkable scenes I have ever witnessed at a football match. Within four minutes Simmons had taken his tally to five and an own goal by Smott had given Alborne an insurmountable 8–0 lead. Incredibly, as the game restarted, Phil Meek's boot caught fire. After it was extinguished by ground staff, a furious row then ensued between the referee and our lads. Athletico argued that with so much spontaneous combustion in the air it was dangerous for the game to continue and the referee should abandon it there and then. Mr Bishop was having none of it, however, and the affair turned ugly for a while with the Alborne goalposts being jostled. In a last ditch attempt to save face, I invaded the pitch on my moped but was thrown off, to howls of laughter, when I hit some particularly nasty divots.

As the game got underway again, Athletico launched their only attack which ended in Gillery's shot from three yards clearing the grandstand by over twenty feet. Alborne seemed content to sit on their eight-goal lead but, when four Whaddon players left the pitch with ten minutes to go so they could catch the last bus, it was too good an opportunity to miss, and Alborne finally ran out winners by eleven goals to nil.

TED COX

THE LES BENCE A-Z OF
FOOTBALL, PART ONE

After days of begging from supporters I have at last compiled a comprehensive A-Z of football, Athletico style.

A = ATTACK

Although fans will tell you there is nothing as exciting as attacking football, those who frequent 'The Tip' have probably never witnessed a game between two attacking sides. With every player in the Whaddon team a potential striker, we tend to concentrate on defence but are always ready to spot the half chance to score a breakaway goal. Sometimes we can go five or six games before spotting a half chance.

B = BACK PASS

In the days of forward, Stanley 'own goal' Reynolds, a back pass was always preferable. This tradition of denying our forwards possession continues today. Possession is nine-tenths of the law and the back pass is safe and sure. This season a new law was introduced, evidently, concerning the passing back to goalies. Well, I have not heard anything.

C = COCK UPS

Trying to push Whaddon into the realms of professional soccer means that all my time, twenty-four hours a day, three days a week, is devoted to the team. But as any great manager knows, delegation to those less capable than he can lead to the occasional administrative hiccup. Having said that, doesn't every club turn up for the wrong match on the right day at least once or twice a season?

D = DEFENSIVE ERRORS

A defence is only as good as its defenders and do not forget that good players do not turn out in non-League football for beer money. In my experience, they are always ruthless, ambitious and dreaming of the lucrative bright lights of Leyton Orient.

E = EVASIVE ACTION

When things are going against him, a manager will often use his cunning to limit the damage. There are a number of ways to get a game abandoned, although streaking across the pitch in only your underpants, as I did at Lake Town last season, is perhaps not the best. Also last season we were due to play Premier Division side Derris Vale in the Cup and doubters said a heavy defeat looked inevitable. However, thanks to my evasive action it did not happen. We failed to turn up.

F = FREE KICK

Apart from a penalty, the free kick is usually a team's best chance of scoring a goal. With an unjustified reputation for less than accurate shooting, our best policy has always been to distract the opposition's concentration on these set pieces. That is why, when we are about to take a free kick, Phil Meek will pull his bottom lip up over his nose and Micky Deere will leap up and down pointing to an imaginary burning Zeppelin.

G = GOALMOUTH INCIDENT

The only one that springs to mind happened at Felton when their goalkeeper and left back got their legs hopelessly tangled and they collapsed in front of Darren Twink who was able to slot the ball home. Unbeknownst to keeper and defender, their laces had been tied together by Sid Dicker, Athletico sponge man and, for this match, replacement linesman.

H = HEADING

Heading for the bar is an integral part of a footballer's social life.

I = INTELLIGENCE

Sadly, as television interviews all too clearly show, most footballers from other teams are monosyllabic in speech and a few yards short of a goal in the brain department. At all levels of the game intelligence is a commodity solely restricted to managers. Two exceptions are Mike Channon and John Motson.

J = JUG LEGS

The late Ken Mentle was reputed to have had such bandy legs, it is said casts were taken by makers of spiral stair rails. His contemporary, Bert Fudge, had knees that pointed precisely east to west, and toes that pointed north to south. He was forced to give up football after stepping on a magnet.

K = KICK-OFF

Every soccer match, from schoolboy level to FA Cup Final at Wembley, starts with a kick-off.

L = LES BENCE

Far-sighted, radical, dedicated. Just three of the qualities I possess that will be invaluable when I get the inevitable call to take up Football League management. As I wander the terraces I often overhear supporters talking about me and the overriding opinion is that 'he won't be here much longer'.

Les Bence. A self portrait in pen and ink

Obviously, you the supporters already accept that I must take the greater challenge when it comes. This is not to say that I will desert the club I love at the first opportunity. No, when I take something on I stick to it, like underpants to a wall.

LES IN CONFIDENCE

WEDNESDAY 3rd MARCH

I hoped a phone call late last night was going to be the chairman of Liverpool offering me the job of manager at Anfield. It turned out to be Terry Wade who had just heard that Trev Proby had been arrested on a number of theft and extortion charges, and had been refused bail. This and our unbelievable performance against Northtown have been the only bright spots in another nightmare week.

Like a twat I decided that attack was the best way of preserving my job, and so I demanded that the board give me complete control over team selection, tactics, welfare etc., with no boardroom interference whatsoever. Surprisingly they agreed and, to show their compliance, said they would leave it up to me to tell Trevor Proby that he was sacked.

Trevor is a man on the fringe of the human race with a very persuasive style, GBH. For the last couple of days I have frantically been trying to work out some sort of compromise, but whichever way I look at it, I just do not have the cash to flee the country. Luckily the police have spared me the ordeal of telling Proby, and also kept my bones intact.

So much for complete bloody control. Pahdra Singh's secretary called earlier to say she would be picking the team for this Saturday's match and that some kid I have never heard of, Ubahni Singh, will be playing centre-forward! Well, no way José was I standing for that. I gave the old bag an ultimatum, either I picked the team or I would quit. She then had the audacity to ask for my resignation in writing. Naturally I withdrew my threat because there is no way I will let Singh and his cronies put one over on Leslie Bence.

There has been a lot of banter in the Supporters' Club lately about the prospect of a supermarket on 'The Tip'. Naturally, those poor, deluded idiots thought that somehow I was in the know as to what was happening. As it brought me an endless supply of free wallop I played along with this. Unfortunately, after the first six or seven freebies things got a little hazy and I understand that I told everyone that Singh and his brothers (no relation) were indeed going to build a superstore on 'The Tip', but that they were also going to spend £2,000,000 on a new stadium for Athletico to be built on top of Mitchley cemetery. Oh, Jesus!

I knew all along of course that Pahdra Singh was only interested in the club for his own profit. You can't pull the bobble hat over my eyes. He knows sod all about football and, talk about stingy, I wish the defence were as tight as the clasp on his wallet. There are, of course, certain charlatans who do receive his grace and favour but, unlike that snake-in-the-grass Pybus, who is always eager to lick Singh's cigar, or smoke his boots, my loyalty cannot be bought. Unless the price is right.

REMEMBER: STOP ACCEPTING DRINKS FROM STRANGERS.

ATHLETICO WHADDON

M/SV.
DIVISION 3

TODAY

· V ·

TWITCHIT
ALBION /
DORNING
TOWN

£1

✻ OFFICIAL PROGRAMME ✻

	P	W	D	L	PTS
GOSLING CELTIC	24	15	5	4	50
CLANSFORD UTD	24	14	4	6	46
ALBORNE	24	12	7	5	43
NORTHTOWN	24	11	6	7	39
SCRIMLEY ARSENAL	24	10	8	6	38
HELLINGBOROUGH	24	10	5	9	35
TWITCHIT ALBION	24	10	4	10	34
FELTON	23	10	4	9	34
REDLAND PARK AVENUE	24	8	9	7	33
SPORTING HYDRA CHEMICALS	24	8	8	8	32
FRAMPTON ROVERS	24	8	7	9	31
DORNING TOWN	23	7	7	9	28
CHAMDEN CITY RESERVES	24	6	9	9	27
SIDCOMBE	24	6	8	10	26
LEECH TOWN	24	6	7	11	25
BOTHAM WDRS	24	6	3	15	21
ATH. WHADDON	22	4	2	16	14

MANAGER'S NOTES

13th March '93

Today we witness a real feast of football here at 'The Tip' when, due to our forced postponement of home games in late November/early December, we play two games in four hours.

When Dorning Town turned up in December they found no one here. Today, however, not only will they meet forty or less baying Athletico fans but also a team primed for a late surge up the League.

My survival plan spun into action the other week with that hard-fought point against Northtown, and although we went down 4–1 against Clansford United I was not unduly worried – every well-oiled engine needs a little fine tuning. I am sure that today my tinkering with Dave Doyle and Phil Meek's positions will prove too much for Dorning Town and the high-flying Twitchit Albion.

*   *   *   *   *   *   *

Let me apologise for the printing errors that will be found on the team sheets in the middle of today's programme. The team line-ups should read as follows:

DORNING TOWN Macey, Burt, Saliki (P.), Raynes, Moles, Hartley, Chambers, Saliki (H.), Weston, Shaw, Harris. Subs. Wolfe, Prosser.

TWITCHIT ALBION Rodborough, Clout, Pearce, Anderson, Millgate, Tavener, Peterson, Ashbone, Bryant, Noad, Wallis. Subs. Rose, Beef.

You will notice on the printed sheet that Ashbone and Wallis of Twitchit are named as goalkeeper and centre-half for Dorning, and that the Saliki twins of Dorning are named as the Twitchit substitutes. Twitchit's actual substitutes, Rose and Beef, are given as substitutes for Dorning. V. Marlow is not included in either squad despite being named as playing for both Dorning, in place of Hartley, and Twitchit, in place of Millgate. V. Marlow is a figment of the printer's imagination.

*　　　*　　　*　　　*　　　*　　　*　　　*

Luckily I am able to correct these mistakes, which is just as well because we face prosecution from the Trading Standards Office after complaints about our programme for the Clansford clash. To put the record straight, I inadvertently misplaced the team sheet sent by Clansford and, to meet the printer's deadline I was forced to make up their team off the top of my head. Surely no supporter actually believed Bobby Charlton, Justin Fashanu and Tom Finney were turning out for United? Even more remarkable, quite a few of you were certain Mike Channon *did* play. Let me make it quite plain, if Mike Channon ever set foot in the Multivite Vegeburger/ Singletons Valve Replacement League Division Three he would not go anywhere but Athletico, even if I had to sell my house and body to keep him here.

*　　　*　　　*　　　*　　　*　　　*　　　*

Finally, following the shock departure of Adie Smith and Jason Pratt (musical differences), we welcome two new faces to the team this afternoon. Kev Knowles has signed from local Jehovah's Witness side Armageddon Wanderers and at his own expense has taken over match programme production, re-naming it the 'Whaddon Watchtower'. Our other new signing is local bricklayer, Billy Lugg. Billy may well be the son of a famous footballer as it has often been rumoured that his mother slept with Plymouth Argyle in the early 1960s.

MULTIVITE VEGEBURGER/ SINGLETONS VALVE REPLACEMENT LEAGUE NEWS

For the third time this season, GOSLING CELTIC manager JIM FISH is our 'Manager-of-the-Month'. Jim is now the lucky owner of his third gold spray valve and now has three years' supply of vegetarian burger bites.

* * * * * * *

Mounting debts look certain to close SIDCOMBE FC. Never a great footballing side, if it was not for the fact that they are in the same League as Athletico Whaddon, they would probably be known as the Athletico Whaddon of Division Three. Our legal department will be in touch – LB

* * * * * * *

Strange but true! COLIN STOKES, the SCRIMLEY ARSENAL goalkeeper once owned a dog that only had three legs!

* * * * * *

A hilarious incident occurred during LITHERWOOD AND CLEGGS home game against REDLAND PARK AVENUE the other week. A number of L and C supporters, decked out in the team's lime green and guava fruit colours, decided to swop hats with predictably side-splitting results. Some found their new hats too small, others discovered they completely covered their eyes and they were unable to watch the match!

Perhaps we are witnessing a new craze on the terraces to rival the inflatable coffins at ATHLETICO WHADDON.

*   *   *   *   *   *   *

Talking of ATHLETICO, League officials are to investigate claims that the trophy cabinet contains a silver vegeburger inscribed 'Manager-of-the-Year Leslie Bence 1992/1993'. This award has not yet been presented and Mr Bence is not even in the reckoning. When questioned, Mr Bence said he had never seen the trophy cabinet in his life, and was at a loss to explain how it came to be in the director's Portakabin. The League have ordered an inquiry.

*   *   *   *   *   *   *

HELLINGBOROUGH centre-half, JOE STOREY, had an embarrassing time on a recent visit to SCRIMLEY ARSENAL. During the match a three-legged dog ran on to the pitch and devoured Joe's shorts. Wearing the briefest of briefs, red-faced Joe played on until the referee, Mr Jones, very kindly removed his own shorts and lent them to Storey.

*   *   *   *   *   *   *

Works team SPORTING HYDRA CHEMICALS have a new manager in Alf Busby. Although in his new post for less than a month, Alf has made such an impression at Polypropylene Park that throughout the League his team are already being nicknamed 'Busby's Test Tube Babes'.

*   *   *   *   *   *   *

Strange but true! After telling ATHLETICO WHADDON goalkeeper, JOHN SLACK, of his Scrimley counterpart's three-legged dog, John informed me that he can top this. He has a dog with four legs.

*   *   *   *   *   *   *

Struggling BOTHAM WANDERERS have called in the police to help in the search for their forward line. A wag in the crowd quipped that it is so long since they have been in evidence, police enquiries are being hampered because no one can name or describe them.

* * * * * * *

I doubt if MICKEY BROWN will forget his trip to CLANSFORD UNITED in a hurry. During the game the FRAMPTON ROVERS full back heard over the tannoy that his wife had given birth to a healthy baby boy. Mickey was so delighted that he promptly scored a hat trick in his side's 4–1 win. But his good fortune did not stop there. On leaving the field, Mickey found a purse containing four pounds, a pension book and a set of house keys. He immediately set off to hand the purse and its contents into the Clansford club office and there he found a distressed but very grateful Mrs Edie Moon (82), Clansford's oldest supporter. What Mickey did not know was that Mrs Moon was so concerned about the loss of her pension book that she had offered £1,000,000 to anyone who found it! Well, it was certainly Mickey's lucky day.

* * * * * * *

As expected, GOSLING CELTIC's £10,000-rated captain, STEWART TRUCKLE, has turned down a move to Third Division ATHLETICO WHADDON. Stewart told us that Whaddon's offer of a free bus pass and as many pizza slices as he could eat if he signed for the club was 'frankly, insulting'.

THE LES BENCE A-Z OF FOOTBALL, PART TWO

Here is the second half of my exclusive A-Z of football, played the Athletico way.

M = MAN FOR MAN MARKING

When talking about marking players only one man can possibly spring to mind, Trevor Proby. During his career that no-nonsense approach has marked players with seventeen black eyes, thirty-six gashed shins, one bruised toe and a broken arm. He has also concussed two linesmen and shot a dog that once ran on to the pitch at Leech.

N = NONE

As in Alborne eleven, Athletico none. Clutton Town nine, Athletico none, etc. etc.

O = OVER THE HILL

When a manager is faced with no financial resources he has to look for youth or experience to fill out his squad. Many ex-professionals prefer to open pubs or manage Swindon Town rather than to ease themselves into retirement by playing non-League football. Always hopeful, I have in the past approached many players with a view to them joining Athletico. Sir Stanley Matthews, Denis Law and Geoff Hurst are unfortunately still to reply. I have, however, had an encouraging response from Emlyn Hughes.

P = PROMOTION

If we wish to progress up the football ladder, I can only see us doing so by winning promotion. Should we ever achieve this, there are those faint hearts who have unkindly suggested the added attraction of pigs flying over 'The Tip'.

Q = QUEUES

The only queues ever seen at 'The Tip' these days are at the tea counter, where 86-year-old Mrs Scricle attempts to deal with thirsty fans. Mrs S. took over from former club skipper, Colin Webley (has he played for Leeds yet?), and her slowness has already become legendary although, in fairness, she is restricted in her movements by a false hip made of Meccano. She is also known for being frugal and will often only serve visiting supporters after running a used teabag three or four times through a mangle.

R = REFEREE

Those of you who know me well may be surprised to learn that I am not anti-referees. It takes a very special person to be a referee. It takes a moron.

S = SUPPORTERS

In ridding the game of these hangers-on we should perhaps take our lead from cricket, a game nobody watches. By kicking-off on Tuesday mornings at 10.30, and continuing the match for three days, we would clear the terraces of this nuisance. Not only that, but think of the score.

When was the last time Whaddon scored 235 goals and lost?

T = TACTICS

Master administrator, father figure, the last hope for flared trousers, these are but a few of the attributes a manager must possess. But most of all he must be a tactical genius able to out-manoeuvre the opposition at a moment's notice. He should also be an accomplished communicator so that players are able to comprehend complicated positional roto-combinations with defensive and forward deviations outside the norm.

U = UNDERSOIL HEATING

Unbelievably, there are some among us who will stop at nothing to keep a game on. In the past, when a postponement was to our obvious advantage, I have had to physically restrain fanatical supporters from going out in freezing conditions to shovel snow off the pitch. Any supporter doing so is now banned for life.

V = VARICOSE VEINS

With so many 'mature' players playing in the Whaddon strip over the years, varicose veins have often been in evidence. Bob Hanley, who played in the 1950s, had a remarkable 56 and, towards the end of his career, Fred Plumb counted 22 on each leg. Not to be outdone, Dave Doyle claimed to have at least 108, but they washed off in the shower.

W = WHADDON AND MITCHLEY ARGUS

The local rag. The *Argus* should stick to printing what it knows best, like the annual flower show or the quaint old custom of rolling the vicar under a bus. Incredible as it may seem, in Mark Crowe the paper has a sports reporter who is unable to hold his drink.

X = XENOPHOBIA

The list of foreign players attracted to Whaddon over the years has been endless. There have been six – Royston Marley, the four Larson brothers and Miguel Romerez. In these six we have proof that not all inhabitants of Jamaica, Sweden and Spain lack the temperament for this country's robust style of play.

Y = YOUTH TEAM

Being a firm believer in the 'start 'em young' policy but desperate for any player I can get to fill out the first team, I have completely overhauled the youth squad. That is to say I have scrapped it.

Z = ZINGIBERACEAE

Plants belonging to the perennial monocotyledonous family of herbs. (All right, I couldn't think of a footballing Z.)

LES IN CONFIDENCE

WEDNESDAY, 10th MARCH

I have decided that now is the time to get tough. And drink more. Both Adie Smith and Jason Pratt phoned to say they had only just heard we have two games on Saturday. This is, they say, a bit inconvenient as they have to meet their girlfriends in the Charles Hawtrey Patio at the Duck and Forceps at midday. It seems they are then off to Birmingham for a Dire Straits concert. Well, in my book nothing comes before football and so I gave them a simple ultimatum: 'Make your choice. It's skiffle or football.'

We are now two players short and I am going to struggle to find eleven men. There are a couple of possibilities. In the massage parlour at lunchtime, Molly Lugg told me her son was now unemployed because his boss, Trevor Proby, was 'in chains' and she would be grateful if I could find him something to do, as he spends all his time kicking his heels, mostly through shop windows in the High Street. I also had a stroke of luck when a Jehovah's Witness called at the door earlier. He asked me if I was willing to let Jehovah into my life to which I replied, 'Only if he can score goals'. This somehow led to a discussion on local football and I discovered that there were eleven fit men and true down at the Kingdom Hall. Not only did this geezer Kev Knowles agree to turn out for us, he also said he would look after the programme as long as he could incorporate a number of religious tracts.

Having scrabbled round picking up as many 'pros' as I can find, and then weighing them against the 'cons', while looking at everything in the most optimistic light, there can be no doubt that we are doomed. Finishing ankle-high in the League is now a pipedream. The foot, the bottom, the abyss, that beckons for the third consecutive season.

I tried to put some money on the 'Stiffs' finishing bottom with the bookies. I thought if I am going to be out of work, I might as well make some cash out of it. Incredibly, it seems they stopped taking bets on Whaddon finishing bottom way before Christmas.

BASTARDS!

ATHLETICO WHADDON

M/SV. DIVISION 3

TODAY
· V ·
ALBOURNE

£1

* OFFICIAL PROGRAMME *

	P	W	D	L	PTS
GOSLING CELTIC	26	17	5	4	56
CLANSFORD UTD	26	14	4	8	46
ALBORNE	26	12	7	7	43
SCRIMLEY ARSENAL	26	11	8	7	41
HELLINGBOROUGH	26	12	5	9	41
TWITCHIT ALBION	27	12	4	11	40
NORTHTOWN	26	11	6	9	39
FELTON	25	11	4	10	37
SPORTING HYDRA CHEMICALS	26	9	9	8	36
FRAMPTON ROVERS	26	9	8	9	35
REDLAND PARK AVENUE	26	8	11	7	35
DORNING TOWN	26	8	8	10	32
SIDCOMBE	26	7	9	10	30
LEECH TOWN	26	7	7	12	28
CHAMDEN CITY RESERVES	26	6	9	11	27
BOTHAM WDRS	26	6	3	17	21
ATH. WHADDON	26	5	2	19	17

MANAGER'S NOTES

3rd April '93

The Lord Jehovah be praised! What a day our 'doubleheader' turned out to be. The one score and three who turned up to see the morning game against Dorning had a real treat. An early goal by the visitors made it look as though we were heading for our nineteenth League defeat of the season, but thanks to my inspirational coaching from the touchline, new boy Kev Knowles levelled the score on the stroke of half-time. With their chins dropping to their shorts, Dorning were unable to match the flair and fitness of a rampant Athletico and Darren Twink's winner, headed in off his new bouffant hairdo, is my choice for 'Goal-of-the-Year'. Sadly, it was inevitable that we could not keep up the pace against Twitchit Albion, especially with so many of our squad approaching the twilight of their careers. The club doctor was a constant fixture on the pitch, applying oxygen and mouth-to-mouth resuscitation. In the circumstances, a 9–0 defeat shows that ordinarily there would be nothing between the teams.

*   *   *   *   *   *   *

No doubt you are all aware of the County FA's decision to relegate the bottom club in Division Three after all. The unfortunate club will drop into a local Sunday League. Although it is early days yet, should we be that club, then it can only spell disaster. The loss of our semi-professional status would bring about a mass exodus of players as many of them rely on their match fees to bolster dole cheques. My own position would also be called into question, as I regard Sunday as sacred.

*   *   *   *   *   *   *

After 55 years at 'The Tip', Athletico will be losing their home at the end of the season. Following Mr Singh's purchase of neighbouring land for a supermarket, it has come to my knowledge that, reluctantly, customer car parking facilities demand that he also purchase 'The Tip' for a car park. As Mr Singh somewhat harshly pointed out, a pitch for a team in our position could be nothing short of a liability. I have moved quickly to secure a ground-sharing scheme with the local comprehensive school. They have a fine pitch although there are no floodlights and the pitch will not be available at weekends. I am sure that, like myself, you will be sorry to leave our old home, scene of many moral victories and one or two actual ones over the years.

*   *   *   *   *   *   *

Our recent spate of away games has yielded plenty of goals but not for the 'Stiffs'. Dorning Town were quick to gain revenge for their defeat here a few weeks ago, by overcoming us 4–0. It is worth noting that had they not scored those four goals the game would have been drawn. The lack of a goalkeeper was exposed most harshly at Felton on Saturday. Thankfully their absent-minded forwards kept the score to a respectable 3–1.

These defeats only heighten the fact that victory today is vital. A week is a long time in football, seven days in fact, but somehow a reversal of February's 11–0 defeat at the hands of today's opponents would prove that Lazarus doesn't have the last word in comebacks, and we are still a team to be reckoned with.

As you know, when the chips are down Leslie Bence comes out fighting. At great personal cost to myself I have recruited the much sought-after Felton Rovers reserve keeper, Igor Pushov. Igor is on loan to us today for 37 minutes and, should he keep a clean sheet, I will have no hesitation in offering him a full contract and the captain's job.

Terry Wade, Whaddon's longest serving player, has decided to retire after today's game. At an emotional meeting earlier this week, Terry told me 'I've lost touch with the modern game, Les, nobody seems to be interested in drinking these days, all they want to do is get on with the football.'

I know many of us agree with these sentiments and perhaps envy Terry for getting out now. His team mates have already made a collection for him and twenty Benson and Hedges, plus two old betting slips allegedly once owned by Lou Macari, will be presented to Terry at half-time.

SPOTLIGHT ON GROUNDHOPPING WITH CHESTER BENCE

Besides being the son of Athletico manager Les Bence, Chester is president of the Whaddon Groundhoppers. This dedicated band of three have given over their lives and wallets to visiting every football ground in the Multivite Vegeburger/Singletons Valve Replacement League. In the following article he attempts to convey some of his enthusiasm for his pastime.

*　　　*　　　*　　　*　　　*　　　*　　　*

Many people reckon we are all a bit loony spending all our spare time going round the non-League grounds of the M/SV but I can think of one really good reason for doing it. It is really brill. When I started, I was very much on my own but over the years it has really caught on in Whaddon and now membership has trebled. If YOU have ever thought of joining, then do not hesitate because it is brilliant.

For your £6 subscription per annum, you get a free bus timetable giving you the times of at least three buses that visit no less than eight M/SV clubs. These timetables are the same as those you get free from the depot but the difference is that the club copies are all signed by my dad and so are brilliant. Also you get a special hat to wear. This is conical in shape and worn when you visit a new ground. On the front of the hat is the letter 'D', this stands for 'done it' i.e. visited the ground.

A small identity card is also issued to each member and this is worth the price of subscription alone. By flashing said card at any M/SV official at any ground you will be at liberty to

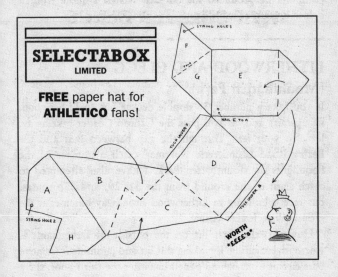

inspect the underside of the grandstand should you be working, as I am, on a survey of all pre-1950 steel structured stands and their method of construction. Similarly, I have found it useful in my research on roof fascia of the Premier Division. In other words, the card is brilliant.

Now if anyone is tempted to join our happy band may I give you some advice which will ensure you get maximum enjoyment from your hobby – specialise. Apart from my own field already mentioned above, others may choose to research Victorian turnstiles, pre-war floodlighting, tea hut menus or programme design; then again, there is still much work to be done on Second Division lavatories. One of our members, my best mate Steve Frost, has a really brilliant speciality which means he never actually visits grounds at all. 'Ground Reconnaissance From Public Transport' is the title of the pamphlet he produced for our last AGM. I quote from it below because it is brilliant.

*   *   *   *   *   *   *

LITHERWOOD AND CLEGG
(Mountbatten Park)

If you take a number 36 double decker bus to Litherwood, sit upstairs and, as you pass the Canton Corner take-away, look to your left. Through the gap between that and the Bezley Road Launderette you may catch a glimpse of the floodlights at Mountbatten Park. I have also attempted to catch sight of the ground from the 31, 29, and 37b routes, but recent building in Litherwood Broadway has meant the ground is no longer visible.

However, the glass lift on the outside of Debenhams is worth investigating. By taking this lift and jamming it (remove blue circuit from behind panel) just after the third floor, there is a good photo opportunity with a glimpse of the cheeky little pink cantilever stand.

BORUSSIA MUNCHEN URCHFONT
SPORTS AND SOCIAL UNITED
(The Welfare Field)

Those of you who jet off to foreign parts for your hols and fly from Chamden airport, may be interested to know that your flight path probably heads out over The Welfare Field.

On a charter flight to Spain last year I spotted the club's ground as we climbed. If I had so wished, I could have climbed out on to the wing and with the use of a telephoto got an unusual shot of the unique S-shaped ground with its mock-Wembley turrets in terracotta. Such a photograph would rank

alongside my snap of Heaven Oak Corinthians Musseldyke
ground director's car park, taken from a rapidly descending
hot air balloon.

THINGLEY BOROUGH VISIGOTHS (Greenwood Lane), FRAMPTON ROVERS (Happy Shopper Leisurerama), CORAN BROTHERS ELECTRIC AND WIRELESS (Linekar Avenue)

By catching the Chamden-London Inter-City train it is possible to go from the Second Division to the Third and back
again on this unequalled trip.

As you pull out of Thingley station this otherwise boring
train ride takes on a whole new significance. On crossing the
viaduct look north-east towards HM Prison – the Greenwood
Lane floodlights are clearly visible for at least 45 seconds.
Then, as the train follows the curve of the track, over the top
of Nettles brewery you can see, by swinging from the luggage
rack, all four gantries.

Passing through Frampton only someone on a completely
different train on a completely different line could fail to see
Rovers' ground in the Happy Shopper Leisurerama complex
with its 24-foot inflatable baked bean can nestling against the
track. If you are unfamiliar with the ground, however, the
stadium itself may well pass you by. The latex medieval cas-
tling in startling black also doubles as the Frampton grandstand and their artificial pitch (100 per cent concrete) lies
below it. Snow White's cottage at the far end is, in actual
fact, the club house and the two giant toadstools are the
players' dressing rooms.

Coran Brothers FC have their ground on the outskirts of
Watley and as the train goes through the middle of the town
you may think it impossible to see any of Linekar Avenue but

this is not so. As the train slows down considerably on the bend, look out beyond the Castoff Carpet Centre (formerly Watley Baptist Chapel) over the spire of Saint Greavsies and you may be able to spot the rusty corrugated sheeting, glistening muddily in the sunlight, that makes up the ground's perimeter fencing.

*   *   *   *   *   *   *

Copies of Steve's pamphlet and his earlier work, 'Spotting Football Grounds From Tall Buildings A Long Way Off Volume 1', are on sale at the club office, price £1.75. They are both brilliant. As well as Steve's publications our newssheet covers such topics as spotting grounds from branch line trains and local buses, and our most recent sheet contained an article on a spectacular view of Northtown's thatched terraces that can be obtained by skateboarding off the top of the multi-storey on to the roof of Lloyds Bank.

*   *   *   *   *   *   *

So as you can see, studying football grounds is a brilliant hobby. Even 'The Tip' which, I must admit, cannot compare with Sporting Hydra Chemicals' spanking new ground, Polypropylene Park, has enough history to make a visit an absorbing day out.

If it is a pastime with a difference that you are after, then why not take up groundhopping. It is brilliant.

CHESTER BENCE

PLEASE NOTE All groundhoppers are expected to wear the following regulation uniform: 'Donovan' canvas cap, blue anorak with Ford Motors logo, brown Crimplene trousers, a battered Liverpool/Spurs/Hendon hold-all, a dog-eared red 'Winfield' notebook with short two-inch pencil, filthy trainers, a hideously expensive camera and a pocket full of Mars bars.

LES IN CONFIDENCE

THURSDAY, 1st APRIL
APRIL FOOLS DAY

Gerry Wills, the Frampton Rovers manager, gave me a ring to say that he had a proposition that may well be to Athletico's advantage. Intrigued, I invited him over and he told me that he was interested in the 'leg-over' possibilities of my back bedroom. It seems he is indulging in some extra physio with the little darling who runs on with the sponge for Frampton. She is insisting that Gerry finds them a 'love nest' a safe distance from his wife. Getting his drift, I willingly agreed as long as he could help me out with my goalkeeper crisis. He did not hesitate in offering me his reserve goalie, the Ukranian, Igor Pushov. 'Iggy' it seems had not settled at Frampton mainly because he did not speak English. Frankly, this surprised me, for as I told Gerry, 'an inability to speak English never hampered Ian St John's football career.' Gerry pointed out, however, that referees were not happy having Pushov and his interpreter stood on the goal line as it gave us an unfair advantage. Agreeing to the deal, I will vacate my pad every Monday evening and every third Sunday.

With the threat of relegation looming again, the loss of the ground, and the millstone around my neck of a team of asthmatic pine martens with the collective brain power of a kiwi fruit, the pressures on me are building to a frightening pitch. The Samaritans have threatened to call in the police if I do not stop pestering them with phone calls, and Alcoholics Anonymous refuse to come out for a drink and discuss my problem.

The Singhs' supermarket swindle has at least got

them out of my bald patch, as the prospect of lots of money has put football right out of their heads. Reg Pybus, with his gun at my head, is always ready to stab me in the back though, and eighteen unlucky defeats has given him plenty of ammunition. I am sure he is the toad behind the unprecedented negative media coverage we are getting at the moment.

My appearance on Radio West's 'Football North' yesterday went well, I thought. It was a stroke of genius on my part to avoid such awkward questions as 'Why has the club such an appalling record?' and 'Is the club's current position due to managerial incompetence?' by pretending it was a terrible phone line and I could not hear the questions. It probably fooled the listeners as only the presenter knew I was actually in the studio.

As for Mark Crowe, the *Argus* sport and nature ramble hack, well, I thought I could expect some loyalty there. His recent article entitled 'Hoof It Bency', apart from being completely devoid of grammar or sentence structure, was one long eulogy in praise of that grass Pybus. Reg used every opportunity to take swipes at me and constantly implied that I had lost the confidence of everybody involved with the club. I telephoned him as soon as I had read the article, and told him that he is facing a very heavy fine for talking to the Press without my permission. Although he pathetically offered me an apology, I remained adamant until we struck a compromise. He told me to get stuffed.

REMEMBER: TELL CHESTER TO GET OUT AND FIND A FLAT BY SUNDAY.

ATHLETICO WHADDON

M/SV. DIVISION 3

TODAY
·V·
FELTON

£1

* OFFICIAL PROGRAMME *

	P	W	D	L	PTS
GOSLING CELTIC	27	18	5	4	59
ALBORNE	27	13	7	7	46
CLANSFORD UTD	27	14	4	9	46
SCRIMLEY ARSENAL	27	11	9	7	42
HELLINGBOROUGH	27	12	6	9	42
NORTHTOWN	27	12	6	9	42
TWITCHIT ALBION	28	12	5	11	41
FELTON	26	11	5	10	38
SPORTING HYDRA CHEMICALS	27	9	10	8	37
FRAMPTON ROVERS	27	9	9	9	36
REDLAND PARK AVENUE	27	8	12	7	36
DORNING TOWN	27	8	9	10	33
SIDCOMBE	27	7	10	10	31
LEECH TOWN	27	7	8	12	29
CHAMDEN CITY RESERVES	27	6	9	12	27
BOTHAM WDRS	27	6	3	18	21
ATH. WHADDON	27	5	2	20	17

MANAGER'S NOTES

10th April '93

Champions 1992/1993 Multivite Vegeburger/Singletons Valve Replacement League Division Three!

Yes, the lads have done it! With four games still to play, the side have clinched the Third Division title and promotion to Division Two.

WELL DONE, GOSLING CELTIC!

We must also extend our congratulations to our neighbours, FC Titford Polymer Converters, for taking the Second Division championship at the first attempt. Being only two miles away, their success has meant that many fair-weather 'Stiffs' supporters have been attracted to their games and in consequence our gate receipts have suffered. Titford have undoubtedly had a great season but I wonder if you have stopped to consider which club has really been the more successful? Benny Polymer, the Titford manager, made it plain at the start of the season that promotion was his goal. Well, he certainly achieved it but remember, winning championships is the easy option. OK, the club benefits in the short term – better gates, better football, bigger income – but that is not how we operate here at Athletico. Neither short- nor long-term success is of any interest to the 'Stiffs', as our record shows.

We are dedicated to experimentation, to pushing back the frontiers of football as we know them, to boldly go where no self-respecting soccer club has gone before, and no, I do not mean the Whaddon and Mitchley Sunday League. Of course paying customers want to see a winning side, and they want superficial honours like League titles and Cup runs, but that is not the Whaddon way. Just look at some of the thought-provoking policies I have introduced this season. By using our budget wisely, I have pioneered the signing of players with obviously limited ability, then groomed these novices, many of whom had never kicked a football before, into first team regulars. I have also advocated holding a bottom three position in the table for as long as possible. Some see this as indicating a constant relegation battle come the winds of March, but I believe it is only from such a lowly position, lulling opponents into a false sense of security, that we can wreak havoc on the rest of the League. The secret of this strategy is, of course, to know when to make that surge up the table before the certainty of relegation sets in. As can be seen from our position at the bottom, it is a secret we have yet to uncover.

*   *   *   *   *   *   *

I have been greatly encouraged by our recent form. The unlucky 4–0 defeat at home to Alborne showed great promise for the future and if it had not been a mathematical impossibility since the beginning of October, I would have said that playing like that we should still be promotion contenders.

*   *   *   *   *   *   *

The great talking point at the Alborne match was the first appearance in many months of our chairman, Mr Pahdra Singh. Despite some unnecessary barracking from supporters, Mr Singh certainly enjoyed himself and got behind the team. In fact, after going three goals down, in sheer desperation Mr Singh ran on to the field, dispossessed an Alborne forward, rounded two defenders and netted in the top left corner. Although I insisted to the referee that the goal should stand because I had sent Pahdra on as substitute, the ref was not fooled, especially as Mr Singh was still wearing his dufflecoat and brogues. Pahdra was escorted from the pitch by a police poodle. Unfortunately, this so incensed some supporters that an ugly incident occurred which was sensationally reported in the *Whaddon and Mitchley Argus* under the banner headline 'Ref Struck by String'.

*   *   *   *   *   *   *

I hope today that all excitement is centred around the Felton goalmouth. If not, let's hope we can complete the double over them and get the game postponed for the second time.

YOUR LINE TO LES

Dear Les,

A few weeks ago we were fortunate enough to meet in a public house where I bought you half a dozen pints and we engaged in a long and fascinating conversation.

During our discussion, you told me that you were about to leave the manager's job at Athletico and take up a similar position with Ipswich Town. You also told me that for eleven years you were national coach and team manager to the United Arab Emirates. Since our meeting I have read nothing about your appointment at Ipswich and believe they are quite happy with their current manager. Also, my *Vauxhall Opal Mints Directory of World Soccer* does not mention your name as ever being connected with the Arab states. How do you explain yourself?

Yours sincerely,
J.T.

Dear J.T.,

To be honest, I do not recall our conversation, or you.

So many people ply me with drinks in the D and F these days that I tend to remember them as I saw them, in a blur.

The Ipswich job was naturally very hush-hush, so I am unable to go into details until my autobiography is published by HMSO in 1999. As to your other query, there is some confusion here I think. The United Arab Emirates that I coached play in the Holtons Sonic Welding Intermediate League (North) and are not a national side at all.

Les Bence

Dear Mr Bence,
I was astonished, to say the least, the other day when I overheard you tell my young son and his friend that Mike Channon, the former Southampton and England footballer, now turned racing magnate, was your brother-in-law.

Well?

Mrs Y. Lamb,
(In disbelief)

Dear Mrs Lamb,
If I had a pound for every time Mr Channon has tried to cash in on my success, I could launch a takeover bid for Manchester United.

He knows full well that we are not related, though he once waved to me from a passing train. As far as I recall from school biology, you do not acquire relatives by waving.

Yours,
Leslie Bence

SPOTLIGHT ON THE ATHLETICO WHADDON CUP RECORD

If League football is a club's bread and butter, then a good Cup run must be the icing on that bread and butter.

Cup games bring relief from the cut and thrust of the League and more importantly can bring much needed revenue to the club. Unfortunately, with a marginally less successful Cup than League record, Athletico have never been in that position. We have however entered a large number of competitions over the years: the FA Cup, FA Vase, County Shield, Debenhams Floodlit Cup and the Sherpa Tensing Van Trophy to name but a few.

THE COUNTY SHIELD

Despite having come a close second to every junior side in the county at least once over the years, as the senior side in the tournament it is hardly surprising that Athletico should have done remarkably well.

Since the club's formation in the 1930s we have reached the first round on no less than 42 occasions. We have reached the second round seven times and the third once. The fourth, fifth, sixth, quarter-final, semi-final and final have, as yet, eluded us.

FA CUP

The greatest of them all. The FA Cup is every club's dream ticket, whatever their status. At the end of our golden period in the 1930s a 2–0 victory over Ditchford Colliery took us past the Preliminary Preliminary First Qualifying Round, although we faltered in the following Preliminary First Qualifying Round, losing 6–2 to Bonsford Hartley of the South FC.

Uniquely, Athletico have had their number slip beneath the lining of the draw hat on no less than four occasions.

FA TROPHY AND FA VASE

Athletico are eligible for both of these tournaments and alternate between the two, one season the Vase, the next the Trophy. Unfortunately, the club seems incapable of deciding which one it is in at any given time. As you may recall, last season we failed to get our name drawn from the Vase hat and, remembering past FA Cup fiascos, I gave the lads the first round Saturday off. It was only by chance that, walking home from the D and F, I spotted our Northern 'opponents', Bleet Town, sitting bewildered in a deserted 'Tip'. They had arrived to play us in the Trophy. The outcome was a £250 fine and disqualification for two seasons.

DEBENHAMS FLOODLIT CUP

Now three seasons old, Athletico had a surprise 2–1 first round victory over Shedford Sunday in the first year, before going out to Nettles 5× Lager/Kellys Spicy Bacon Bites Division One champions, AFC Brampton by seven goals to less.

Last season, of course, we fancied our chances of reaching the second round quite comfortably as our opening opponents were lowly Hellingborough. During a nail-biting second half, with the score 1–1 to the 'Whads', the floodlight collapsed on to the goalposts. This caused them to sink into the ground until the crossbar was only two inches above the grass. The game was abandoned, Athletico fined £270 and the club was disqualified from the competition for two seasons.

LES IN CONFIDENCE

WEDNESDAY, 7th APRIL

After reading my just completed programme notes for this Saturday, I have decided that spending money on a creative writing course at the Tech. would be a waste of money. I am a natural.

Reluctantly, I attended the celebration at the Docherty Suite, Titford, for Polymers Championship. Although I had a mouthful of sour grapes I thought it was worth going so I could corner Polymers football club chairman, Stan Bates. Having received no reply from Wrexham to my offer of taking over as manager, I have decided to set my sights a little lower, hence my chat with Stan. I told Bates straight out that I was the only man who had the vision and know-how to keep his club in the First Division and that for a reasonable salary, say 15K a year, I would be willing to quit Athletico. Naturally I approached Bates in the strictest confidence, but all too quickly I learned that he is just a gin-sodden loud-mouth. Within minutes my offer was all over the Docherty Suite, and I became the source of hysterical laughter, ridicule and abuse. Humiliated, I made my excuses – dinner with Mike Channon – and left.

On returning home I retired, tucking myself up in bed with a hot toddy bottle. I had not been counting own goals for more than a few minutes when I heard extraordinary sounds coming from my wardrobe. Switching on my bedside lamp, I picked up a heavy, blunt instrument (*The Rothmans Football Yearbook 1986/87*) and tore open the door. There, crouching among my nylon shirts and 'World Cup Willy' T-shirt collection were Mark Crowe and an *Argus* photographer.

Crowe offered a pathetic excuse about investigating woodworm infestation for his nature column, but I soon beetled the truth out of him. He told me that in my back bedroom was a sensational sports story of sex, drugs and liniment. He believed an, as yet unidentifiable, soccer manager was using my house for adulterous purposes with a young female on his staff. Naturally, I told him his suspicions were preposterous and, even if they were true, I would never betray a fellow professional. Crowe then had the vulgar audacity to offer me a pitiful ten quid if I revealed the manager's name. I viewed his offer with utter contempt and told him 'Gerry Wills, Frampton Rovers'.

The arrogance of some of the has-beens in the Athletico squad is pathetic. This week alone, Twink, Doyle, Pollock, Smott and Deere have all said they will not be playing for the 'Stiffs' next season as they are TOO GOOD for Sunday League football! Well, if they think they are going to follow me into the Multivite/Singletons First Division when I take over at Titford Polymers, then they are going to be bloody disappointed.

ATHLETICO WHADDON

M/SV. DIVISION 3

TODAY

· V ·

LEECH TOWN

£1

✳ OFFICIAL PROGRAMME ✳

	P	W	D	L	PTS
GOSLING CELTIC	29	20	5	4	65
ALBORNE	29	14	8	7	50
CLANSFORD UTD	29	15	4	10	49
HELLINGBOROUGH	29	13	7	9	46
NORTHTOWN	29	13	6	10	45
SCRIMLEY ARSENAL	29	11	9	9	42
TWITCHIT ALBION	30	12	6	12	42
SPORTING HYDRA CHEMICALS	29	10	11	8	41
REDLAND PARK AVENUE	29	9	12	8	39
FELTON	28	11	6	11	39
DORNING TOWN	29	9	10	10	37
FRAMPTON ROVERS	29	9	9	11	36
SIDCOMBE	29	8	11	10	35
LEECH TOWN	29	8	8	13	32
CHAMDEN CITY RESERVES	29	7	10	12	31
BOTHAM WDRS	29	6	3	20	21
ATH. WHADDON	29	6	2	21	20

MANAGER'S NOTES

17th April '93

What a week! I have always said football is unpredictable unless you know what is going to happen.

Last weekend we were caught in a fierce struggle with Felton. A minute to go, 1–1, Meek netting in the first half, when an open goal stares Darren Twink in the face. His shot hits the corner flag, rebounds on to the crossbar and 'Twinky' is there to smash home the winner with his tummy. ATHLETICO 2, FELTON 1! The score was even more remarkable because we played well below our best. As you know, I am a manager who has never shirked from putting a player's welfare before football and, unlike many less tolerant managers, I was quite happy for Steve Gillery to hold his stag 'night' at 10 a.m. on the morning of the match, albeit a game crucial to our survival. Unfortunately, although a good time was had by all, a number of the team picked up a strange flu bug. Black coffee and treacle soup flowed in abundance before kick-off but a number of players obviously played with extremely high temperatures. This explains our erratic performance and the peculiar antics of Steve Gillery who insisted on wearing his shorts on his head, and 'Mig' Romerez who was booked for kissing a linesman. Luckily, Felton were at full strength, so we had little chance of losing.

*　　　*　　　*　　　*　　　*　　　*　　　*

Following Botham Wanderers' defeat, we now move off the bottom for the first time in four months. The victory over Felton certainly got the 'Stiffs' buzzing at Sporting Hydra Chemicals on Tuesday night but, sadly, we failed to respond to their 5–0 half-time lead. I had pulled the team together by the second half, and Sporting found us a very different proposition and were lucky to hold us to 0–0. In fact, if they had not scored those early five goals they would not have won.

We should, of course, be going into today's game with Leech Town knowing that only a victory will keep us in the League. THIS IS NOT SO. I can now reveal that if we remain second from bottom we will not be relegated. This is all due to Sidcombe having resigned from the League. We do not, of course, wish to gloat, having come close to liquidation many times ourselves, but it has to be said, WELL DONE, SID-COMBE!

*   *   *   *   *   *   *

As you are no doubt aware, a new League ruling states that a point will be deducted for every ineligible player a club fields. Not wishing to take chances at this critical time in the season, I have had to drop four regulars from the side today. This makes team selection difficult and the problem has been heightened by my sacking of club coach, Reg Pybus. Reg gave his life and soul to this club, plus an extra 110 per cent per match, but unfortunately he chose to undermine my authority in such a way that I was forced to demand his dismissal by the board.

Rumours will no doubt circulate throughout the town and, as a figure of authority within the club, I am sure the artisans on the terraces will side with Reg, but let me put forward my reason for sacking him. Without my knowledge or authorisation, Reg took it upon himself to hand the Press a list of star names I was proposing to bring to the club. He suggested that should these signings go through, the club would be plunged into bankruptcy. The local gutter press, the *Whaddon and Mitchley Argus*, then printed the following names of players I hoped to sign – C. Flower, Tom Atoes and a mysterious Russian, Ham Tinof. This action of Reg's was totally irresponsible on two counts. Firstly, I have been in football management long enough to know that team changes at this late stage will do nothing for the confidence of existing players. Secondly, what he actually published was my supermarket shopping list. I know back in the 1930s Bradford City had a full back called McLuggage, but surely not even Reg believes that somewhere out there is a left back called Halfpound O'Liver.

*　　　*　　　*　　　*　　　*　　　*　　　*

May I urge you all to generously support today's raffle. In all my years at the club I cannot remember such a sensational line up of prizes as are on offer here.

FIRST PRIZE A chicken egg.

SECOND PRIZE Four cooking apples.

THIRD PRIZE A box of matches (minimum contents 65).

PHEW!

TRY

Greavsie's

PORK PIES

"they're evil!"
SAYS RESERVE **ATHLETICO**
STRIKER *Gummy Woods*

RUBBER PASTRY ✱ ADDED 'E'
NUMBERS ✱ FINEST OFFAL

SUPPORTERS' CLUB NEWS

Despite an increase in attendance this year, our annual club dinner last Friday evening was a very mixed affair.

Mrs Mentle, the widow of her late husband, gave a short introductory speech in praise of him and his achievements for the club. A number of younger members present, already the worse for drink, interrupted her speech on a number of occasions as they chanted 'Bring on the stripper' and 'Let's get inflation down to nought per cent'. Obviously distressed, Mrs Mentle cut short her speech and forgot to present the 'Player-of-the-Year' award. In fact, no player received the required three votes to qualify and in the players' 'Player-of-the-Year' award each player voted for himself. However, 160 supporters voted for Trevor Proby, but as he is no longer a member of the club those votes were declared void.

The meal then followed and all had their fill of sausage rolls and crisps, washed down with delicious barley water. A number of guests, unaccustomed to attending formal functions, caused a few unpleasant moments when they began targeting abuse at social secretary, the Reverend Shrigley. The main substance to their complaints was that at £26 a ticket they were not receiving value for money. The good 'Rev.' attempted to pacify them by pointing out that the evening was a glorious opportunity to meet the players in an informal atmosphere, and to buy their heroes a drink. This only seemed to exasperate the situation and it was some time before order was restored.

Supporters' Club member, Jack Mattock, then presented a slide show entitled 'My Favourite Ferrets'. Jack, who has been breeding ferrets for more than forty years, showed us soft focus shots of brown ferrets, white ferrets, ferrets eating mice and ferrets building their nests in old Athletico programmes. His thirty-minute ramble was greatly appreciated by all present, as it enabled many to sleep off their pre-meal excess of Nettles. Regrettably, it also gave those 'Bog End' supporters present a chance to run loudly through their repertoire of football chants and sea shanties.

The main event of the evening was a speech by Mr Leslie M. Bence, currently team manager. A number of guests and most players left at this point and so missed the 'Boss' deliver a riveting talk entitled 'Taylor, Channon and Bence'.

Les had us all on the edge of our seats and those who remained found their voices again, encouraging Les with a deafening cry of 'Bring back the ferrets'. The climax came when a show of hands was asked for to vote on a proposal that the evening's raffle prize, a cuddly soap dish, be replaced by the manager's job. When the motion was carried, bottles and fists began to fly and unfortunately Mr Bence was ejected when the police had to be called.

Those remaining then went home after the Queen. (The anthem that is, not Her Majesty, who failed to reply to our invitation to deliver the Ken Mentle Memorial Lecture.)

*　　　*　　　*　　　*　　　*　　　*　　　*

Jones and Pratley, the motor coach company, have told Supporters' Club officials that they will no longer be able to hire their coaches for away games. A service bus, number 58, will get you to Gosling for our last away match of the season. There are two buses a day from Whaddon which leave outside the nuclear shelter at 6.15 a.m. or 7.34 p.m. The only return bus (Gosling-Whaddon) leaves at midday. Next season, the Supporters' Club hope to start up a bicycle hire scheme for away matches. This will include special six-seater machines for those who like to travel in organised gangs.

LES IN CONFIDENCE

WEDNESDAY, 14th APRIL

Things started so well at the weekend I knew it could not last. The win over Felton still hasn't sunk in. All I can say is, it is a good job players are not breathalysed before a match, because all of us were completely smashed! Thanks to the rank stupidity of Steve Gillery's bride-to-be, he had to hold his stag night on Saturday morning and rush off to the ceremony during half-time in the afternoon. Well, some of us in football still have principles and one of mine is never to refuse a drink. This is also a belief held by my squad and so, neck-high in wallop, come three o'clock we were eleven hangovers in search of a kick around. Somehow, Reg Pybus, who is such a square he even has a mono Walkman, refused to drink with the match only hours away, and so managed to get the team into their kit and out on to the pitch. I remember nothing whatever about the match, as I passed out thirty yards from the ground.

On Sunday I heard that Sidcombe have gone to the wall. This must surely mean we will not be relegated. As I told Denny d'Arcy, the Sidcombe manager, when I rang up to say good riddance, 'We are just the amoeba on the European footer lake. Clubs like ours have to try and survive on the crumbs washed from bread tossed in by the business world, to feed the mallards of the Football League.'* Still, as Sidcombe stuffed us twice this season they can go to hell. Sod solidarity!

While I was out, Reg Pybus dropped in a note saying he had been invited to Wrexham with a view to joining them as coach. Before splicing a dozen lagers, I was on

* © Les Bence 1993

the blower to Reg to tell him that hencewith and fore-forth he was no longer an employee of Athletico Whad-don. He suggested I violently introduce a turnip up my rectum because I no longer have the power to hire or fire anybody. At his own suggestion, Reg said Singh had personally removed that clause from my contract with his nail clippers. It makes me want to puke, except I did enough of that last Saturday night! Some cretins like Pybus are only in football for what they can get out of it. Well, as far as I am concerned Reg is sacked and I shall say so in the programme. No doubt when Wrex-ham see what a joke he is, he will be back at 'The Tip' licking a few supporters' backsides and begging for his job back.

Thank God the cricket season is almost with us. We have three more games to go before I can relax and set about re-negotiating my pitiful contracts at the club and the DSS.

I have had to stoop to pocketing the money the Sup-porters' Club give for raffle prizes. They gave me 25 quid this week but I rummaged through the shed and found a couple of things to stick in as prizes. In fact, the four cooking apples should have been five, but our continuing cashflow problems meant I had to disguise one of them as the reserve match ball.

ATHLETICO -WHADDON

M/SV. DIVISION 3

TODAY
·V·
HELLINGBOR O'

£1

* OFFICIAL PROGRAMME *

	P	W	D	L	PTS
GOSLING CELTIC	31	22	5	4	71
ALBORNE	31	15	9	7	54
CLANSFORD UTD	31	16	5	10	53
SCRIMLEY ARSENAL	31	13	9	9	48
NORTHTOWN	31	14	6	11	48
HELLINGBOROUGH	31	13	8	10	47
FELTON	31	12	7	12	43
TWITCHIT ALBION	31	12	7	12	43
SPORTING HYDRA CHEMICALS	31	8	12	11	42
FRAMPTON ROVERS	31	10	10	11	40
REDLAND PARK AVENUE	31	9	13	9	40
DORNING TOWN	31	9	11	11	38
LEECH TOWN	31	9	9	13	36
CHAMDEN CITY RESERVES	31	7	11	13	32
ATH. WHADDON	31	6	2	23	20
BOTHAM WDRS	31	6	4	21	19*

* 2 points deducted.
SIDCOMBE resigned.

MANAGER'S NOTES

1st May '93

No doubt an air of sadness will pervade our match with old rivals Hellingborough today. Not only is it our last match of the season but also the last match to be played at 'The Tip'.

We go into next season, however, full of hope and with a carefree spirit. After our dour 3–0 defeat against Leech, we certainly had that carefree spirit in our midweek encounter with champions Gosling Celtic. I for one was heartened to see us just going out there and enjoying ourselves, despite going down by eight goals to one. Unfortunately, some of our supporters who had hiked to the match appeared not to have a sense of humour. With Botham Wanderers already relegated and our position safe, we will adopt this carefree attitude again today so expect to see GOALS! GOALS! GOALS!

*   *   *   *   *   *   *

Looking back over the season it seems to me supporters can have little cause for complaint. Although promotion slipped from our grasp early on, our fight for survival over the last seven months has been real nail-biting stuff. Let me assure you, I never had the slightest doubt we would stay in Division Three. As I have often said in these 'Notes', Athletico is a forward-looking club and so thoughts must now turn to next season. Already the club have appointed a new coach to replace that disgraced old stager, Reg 'Accrington Stanley' Pybus. He is Mr Anka Singh who has been in coaching for many years, running the Golden Sunset minibus hire company.

*   *   *   *   *   *   *

Our groundshare next season will show what the team is

really made of as we run out for home games on the unfamiliar battlefield of St Dodimeads Comprehensive. With the pitch being unavailable during term time, three-quarters of our games will be away. Travelling to these matches could, of course, prove expensive and some of our senior supporters may find they are unable to afford it. This could be to the club's advantage in the long-run, however, because with supporters at a loose end on Saturdays, they have an ideal opportunity to visit the 'old home' and Mr Singh's new megastore. In so doing, they will increase our chairman's profit margin and this in turn means he will be able to give me a three-figure budget with which to entice quality players.

*　　　*　　／*　　　*　　　*　　　*　　　*

During the close season I will be contributing no less than 119 per cent of my energy to the club. My time will be spent planning new tactical strategies and introducing a far-reaching training programme which will, I am sure, inevitably lead to a complete rewriting of the Football Association's *Don Howe Coaching Manual*. On my advice, the board have determined to sweep a new broom through the club, and wheely-bin those who no longer make the grade. As a matter of fact, directly after today's game I will be going into frank discussions with the chairman to search out the real dead wood.

Looking forward to next season.

Les Bence (manager).

MULTIVITE VEGEBURGER/ SINGLETONS VALVE REPLACEMENT LEAGUE NEWS

AFC DIPLOCK held a novel celebration before the kick-off of their match against NAGGS BOTTOM CELTIC last Saturday.

'The Sidings' ground is built on the site of the old Diplock railway station which was closed in 1967. A small crowd gathered on the pitch to commemorate April 1963, when the Beatles passed through on a train to somewhere else. A number of 'We luv Paul' and 'John is fab' banners were in evidence and Diplock defender, TONY SMART, actually fainted.

*　　　*　　　*　　　*　　　*　　　*　　　*

Enterprising NORTHTOWN have signed Japanese international, Itsibitsi Takamoto. 'Itsi' won his cap eighteen years ago, coming on in the dying seconds of an 8–1 victory over Hong Kong. Mr Takamoto is an engineer at the Northtown Nissan plant and in his spare time enjoys building robots. Provided clearance is given by the League, Northtown manager, Norman Blick, hopes to introduce a number of them into his squad next season.

*　　　*　　　*　　　*　　　*　　　*　　　*

The ATHLETICO WHADDON board have instigated a new local Cup competition. With one exception, the Ken Mentle Cup is only open to school sides in the Whaddon and Mitchley area. The one exception is the Athletico first team. Whaddon boss, Les Bence, told us 'The competition might seem one-sided what with all the other teams being school sides and us also getting a bye until the semi-finals, but I am determined to see at least one cup in our cabinet this season.'

*　　　*　　　*　　　*　　　*　　　*　　　*

The large crowd that crammed into the new men's toilets at COLDALE TROJANS ground last month were disappointed that guests of honour, the Nolan Sisters, failed to turn up for the opening. As one wag put it, as it was the opening of the toilets, perhaps they should have invited Lou Macari.

*　　　*　　　*　　　*　　　*　　　*　　　*

A proposed merger between First Division HOTTON FARM COLLIERY RESERVES and their neighbours, BORUSSIA MUNCHEN URCHFONT SPORTS AND SOCIAL UNITED, has been scrapped.

Both clubs agreed that a team called Borussia Munchen Urchfont and Hotton Farm Colliery Sports and Social United Reserves was stupid.

*　　　*　　　*　　　*　　　*　　　*　　　*

So many fans are turning up to see Premier side CHAMDEN CITY these days that the club has been forced to buy the neighbouring supermarket. They hope to demolish the store and build a bar extension, behind the main stand, in its place.

*　　　*　　　*　　　*　　　*　　　*　　　*

Supporters of BOTTS COMMON CORINTHIANS will no longer have to put up with annoying cancellations or last-minute postponements because of a frost-ravaged pitch during the winter months. The club has disbanded.

*　　　*　　　*　　　*　　　*　　　*　　　*

HELLINGBOROUGH are holding a beer and skittles seminar next Thursday evening for budding footballers. The event will go under the title 'Dribbling for Beginners'.

* * * * * * *

STOP PRESS The Ken Mentle Trophy was won by Mitchley Comprehensive, who beat the Mother Theresa Convent School 3–2 in a hard-fought final.

LES IN CONFIDENCE

WEDNESDAY, 5th MAY

Pahdra Singh mounted the pavement in his Bentley this morning and pinned me to the window of the Wimpy Bar. As I struggled free he thrust an envelope into my mouth and then drove off. The note was short and to the point. 'Les, re-Athletico manager, you're sacked.'

I was still in a bewildered stupor of anger and disbelief when that Wrexham reject, Reg Pybus, called round to see me. I thought he came round to gloat and I was right. The pot-bellied tosser told me that the club wished to make a gesture in recognition of all I had done for the 'Stiffs' during my spell as manager, and after much discussion it was agreed that they could best show their appreciation by raising the price of my season ticket for next year by 25 per cent. Thanks Reg, you're a brick.

Despite bordering on acute alcoholic poisoning, somehow my sacking still hasn't sunk in. This afternoon I made what is perhaps my last visit to 'The Tip'. I stood looking at the pools of water lying on the pitch, the door of the directors' Portakabin swinging back and forth on its one remaining hinge, and I recalled the good times, remembered the bad. The wins, the defeats and more defeats. Although I am down, I still have my pride and dignity and so I thought it only right that I should remove all the silverware I had brought to the club from the trophy cabinet: my cycling proficiency medal, the Mitchley Majorettes runners-up trophy I nicked from their carnival float, my Winston Churchill commemorative coin and the photograph of Michel Platini and myself talking football outside Broadcasting

House whilst both waiting to secure Bruce Forsyth's autograph.

Still dazed and confused, I wandered over the bare earth that was once the Ken Mentle Memorial Stand. My lips quivered as I entered the small, plastic road-sweeper's hut which now acted as the home team's changing room. Familiar smells rose above the ever-present odour of the nearby sewage farm, and tears came into my eyes as my nostrils sniffed out stale liniment, old Bovril and the lingering aroma of Dave Doyle's feet.

After one last, loving look at the 'old home', I walked through the turnstiles and broke down. (For crissakes! I told the club those gates had rusted and would cause an injury, but would they bloody listen?) As I dragged myself back to the Duck and Forceps, I suddenly felt a strange empathy with the great Mike Channon. Here we both are, two footballing Doris Stokeses, two men out of time. Two stadium-sized managerial talents holding half-time team talks while the rest of the soccer world has not even kicked off yet. If the Empire State Building of English football, the FA Premier League, cannot recognise Mike's ability in management, then what hope has my talent, three blocks away on the taxi rank, where the Multivite/Singletons Division Three languishes.

Unlike Mike, however, I shall not turn my back on the game I love. I am ready and willing to take anything football can throw at me. As Brian Clough told me when I met him on the top of the Little Elm bus earlier this season — we were both going to check out Little Elm Intaflora's young Dutch forward, Kylie Van Der Graaf — 'Sadly, young man, football is like a football.' How right you were, Brian. I have certainly been kicked in the teeth by those Whaddon bastards.

Damn it! I gave my every waking hour to that club unless I was doing something else. I poured my heart, soul and a couple of vats from Nettles brewery into making it a cohesive, disciplined goal-scoring machine, only to see my dream sabotaged by soccer-illiterate shopkeepers and eleven Lego-legged, sloth-brained idiots in vaguely matching shorts. Christ! Did I not, knowing the perilous financial state of the club, refuse to take a pay rise in line with my Social Security increase?

I am not looking for, or expecting, sympathy, but as I have selflessly ridden through the valley of the Multivite Vegeburger/Singletons Valve Replacement League Division Three, I have taken abuse to the left of me and phlegm to the right.

I think it was John Motson who once said 'That's it. It's all over. No, it's not.' In the Hattie Jacques Cocktail Bar tonight, there are probably wry smiles on the faces of those who think they have seen the last of Leslie Bence rucking into the hurly-burly of football management. They are probably right.

Well, sod 'em.

ATHLETICO WHADDON F.C.

REQUIRE A

PLAYER/MANAGER
MANAGER

Apply; Mr P. Singh, c/o
McMenemy Villas, Whaddon

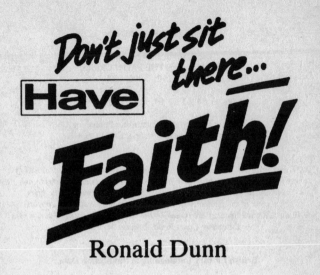

Don't just sit there...
Have Faith!

Ronald Dunn

alpha

Copyright © Ronald Dunn

Published in 1994 by Alpha
(First published as THE FAITH CRISIS)
Reprinted 1994, 1995, 1996, 2000, 2001

07 06 05 04 03 02 01   12 11 10 9 8 7 6

Alpha is an imprint of Paternoster Publishing,
PO Box 300, Carlisle, Cumbria, CA3 0QS, UK

*All rights reserved. No part of this publication may be reproduced, stored in a
retrieval system, or transmitted in any form or by any means, electronic,
mechanical, photocopying, recording or otherwise, without the prior
permission of the publisher or a licence permitting restricted copying.
In the UK such licences are issued by the copyright Licensing Agency, 90
Tottenham Court Road, London, W1P 9HE*

British Library Cataloguing in Publication Data

A catalogue record for this book is available from the British Library

ISBN 1-898938-96-2

Unless otherwise indicated Scripture quotations are taken from the
HOLY BIBLE, NEW INTERNATIONAL VERSION
Copyright © 1973, 1978, 1984 by the International Bible Society.
Used by permission of Hodder and Stoughton Limited. All rights reserved.
'NIV' is a registered trademark of the International Bible Society
UK trademark number 1448790
Scripture quotations marked RSV are from
THE HOLY BIBLE, REVISED STANDARD VERSION
© 1952 National Council of the Churches of Christ. Published by Thomas
Nelson and Sons, Nashville, Tennessee
Scripture quotations marked AV are from the AUTHORISED VERSION
Scripture quotations marked MLB are from
THE MODERN LANGUAGE BIBLE, THE NEW BERKELEY VERSION
© 1959, 1968 by Zondervan Bible Publishers, Grand Rapids, Michigan

Printed in Great Britain by
Cox and Wyman Limited, Reading

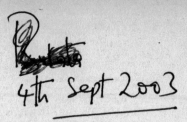

4th Sept 2003

This
is for

K A Y E

who
never
stopped
believing

Contents

The author wishes to acknowledge the following publications and publishers for materials quoted in this book:

All of Grace by C. H. Spurgeon. Copyright 1978 by Moody Press.

The Biblical Doctrine of Heaven by Wilbur M. Smith. Copyright 1968 by Moody Press.

Does God Still Guide? by J. Sidlow Baxter. Copyright 1968 by the Zondervan Corporation.

The Epistle of James by C. Leslie Mitton. Copyright 1966 by William B. Eerdmans Publishing Company.

The Epistle of St. Paul to the Galatians by J. B. Lightfoot. Copyright 1962 by the Zondervan Corporation.

The Epistle to the Romans by A. C. Headlam and William Sanday. Copyright 1901 by Charles Scribner's Sons.

The Epistle to the Romans, Volume II by John Murray. Copyright 1965 by William B. Eerdmans Publishing Company.

Evangelism in a Tangled World by Wayne McDill. Copyright 1976 by Broadman Press.

The Exploration of Faith by R. E. O. White. Copyright 1969 by Moody Press.

An Expository Dictionary of New Testament Words by W. E. Vine. Copyright 1940 by Fleming H. Revell Company.

Kneeling We Triumph by Edwin and Lillian Harvey. Copyright 1974 by Moody Press.

The Law of Faith by Norman Grubb. Copyright 1947 by the Christian Literature Crusade.

Let's Live by Curtis C. Mitchell. Copyright 1975 by Fleming H. Revell Company.

A Linguistic Key to the Greek New Testament, Volume II by Fritz Rienecker. Copyright 1980 by the Zondervan Corporation.

My Utmost for His Highest by Oswald Chambers. Copyright 1935 by Dodd, Mead & Company, Inc.

The New American Standard Bible. Copyright 1960, 1962, 1963, 1968, 1971, 1972, 1973, 1975, 1977 by the Lockman Foundation.

9

The New Testament in the Language of the People by Charles B. Williams. Copyright 1937, 1966 by Edith S. Williams. Moody Press.

The New Testament in Modern English, rev. ed., J. B. Phillips, trans. Copyright 1958, 1960, 1972 by J. B. Phillips. Macmillan Publishing Co., Inc.

New Testament Words by William Barclay. Copyright 1976 by Westminster Press.

The Path of Prayer by Samuel Chadwick. Copyright 1931 by Hodder & Stoughton, London.

A Pocket Lexicon to the Greek New Testament by Alexander Souter. Copyright 1956 by Oxford University Press.

Prayer Power Unlimited by J. Oswald Sanders. Copyright 1977 by Moody Press.

Revival in Romans by Walter K. Price. Copyright 1962 by the Zondervan Corporation.

Romans: A Study Guide Commentary by Bruce Corley and Curtis Vaughan. Copyright 1976 by the Zondervan Corporation.

The Screwtape Letters by C. S. Lewis. Copyright 1942 by C. S. Lewis. Macmillan Publishing Co., Inc.

The Temper of Our Time by Eric Hoffer. Copyright 1967 by Harper & Row, Publishers, Inc.

A Theological Workbook of the Bible edited by Alan Richardson. Copyright 1950, and renewed 1978, by Macmillan Publishing Co., Inc.

Though I Walk Through the Valley by Vance Havner. Copyright 1974 by Fleming H. Revell Company.

'Through It All' by Andraé Crouch. Copyright 1971 by Manna Music, Inc., 2111 Kenmere Ave., Burbank, CA 91504.

The Vocabulary of the Greek Testament by George Milligan and James Moulton. Copyright 1930 by William B. Eerdmans Publishing Company.

Weymouth's New Testament in Modern Speech by Richard Francis Weymouth. Special arrangement with James Clarke & Company, Ltd. Reprinted by permission of Harper & Row, Publishers, Inc.

What Demons Can Do to Saints by Merrill F. Unger. Copyright 1977 by Moody Press.

Prologue

I met a man who walked by faith. Physically, his walk was slow, halting, at times more of a shuffle than a walk, for he had been condemned to death by three terminal diseases.

And so I watched this man who walked by faith and waited for the miracle. But the miracle of healing did not come. I was surprised but he wasn't, for God had promised him a greater miracle–the miracle of life sustained in the midst of sickness and suffering. Alive by His life, was the way he put it.

And so I watched this man who walked by faith live twenty years beyond the doctors' predictions and demonstrate to thousands around the world that it truly means to live by faith.

He loved to quote Jesus' words in John 6. When asked, 'What shall we do, that we may work the works of God?', Jesus answered, 'This is the work of God that you believe in Him whom He has sent.' In a day of seeking after signs and wonders, when only the spectacular is considered miraculous, we need to be reminded that the greatest thing you and I can do for God is simply to believe on Him.

Some words are like drapes that have faded from long exposure to the sun. Frequent use and misuse has drained the colour from their meaning until they are no longer recognizable. Such words need, from

11

time to time, to be reexamined to insure their use is consistent with their meaning.

Faith is a word dangerously close to fading. The word itself must be healed before it can bring healing to others.

Many Christians confuse the key of faith with counterfeit keys, keys that bear a remarkable resemblence to faith but are actually look-alike replicas. Often what they judge to be faith is in fact presumption, or wishful thinking, or selfish desire, or a denial of reality or some form of positive thinking. And when these bogus keys fail to open the doors of God's promises, some conclude that they are not of the 'chosen few' and abandon any hope of living the life of faith.

But real faith never fails to open the door; it always achieves its goal. The question, then, is what is true faith? And how do we tell the difference between the true and the false?

A few years ago I met a man whose son worked for the Treasury Department. He told me he asked his son how the government trained them to spot counterfeit money. 'I expected my son to say they studied the techniques of known counterfeiters, samples of phony money, and so forth,' he said. But his son told him they learned to spot the counterfeit by studying real currency. 'We get to know the real thing so well,' he told his father, 'that it's easy to spot the phony.'

And that is what this book is about—we want to

study the real thing, to get to know it so well, so thoroughly, that we will be saved from deception and be able to master the art of living by faith.

—

PART ONE

Faith
Examined

—

CHAPTER ONE

The House That Grace Built

Salvation is like a house built beside a broad and busy highway. Like everyone else, I was born on that highway and was spending my life following it to its destination. At first the trip had been exciting and almost effortless, the constant flow of the crowd carrying me along. But the farther down the road I got the more difficult things became; my original joy had dissipated and I noticed that my fellow travellers rarely laughed anymore and their occasional smiles seemed forced. The backpack I had been issued at the beginning of my journey had grown heavier each day and I was now permanently stooped from its weight. Worst of all, I had been overtaken lately by an unexplainable fear of reaching the end of the highway.

One day my attention was drawn suddenly to the side of the highway to a magnificently constructed house. Over its narrow front doors a sign silently announced in bold red letters:

'WHOSOEVER WILL MAY ENTER
AND FIND REST.'

I don't know how I knew it, but I realized that if I

could reach the inside of this beautiful house I would be saved from the highway and its destination. Pushing my way through the mass of indifferent travellers, I broke clear of the crowd and ran up the steps to the front door. But it was locked. *Perhaps it's only stuck*, I thought, and tried again. It refused to open. I was confused. Why would someone put up a sign inviting people in and then lock the door to keep them out? Not knowing what else to do (I refused to return to the highway), I pounded on the door, shouted for someone on the inside to open it, and tried to pick the lock–but it was useless.

Suddenly a voice spoke my name and I spun around. It was the Builder of the House. He placed in my hand a key on which was carved one word: FAITH.

Turning back to the door, I inserted the key in the lock, twisted it, and heard a reassuring click. The door swung open and I stepped across the threshold. Immediately the backpack fell from my shoulders, my back began to straighten like a wilting flower reaching for the sunlight, and from deep within me my soul breathed a sigh of relief as an extraordinary sense of peace and well-being wrapped itself around me.

The Builder of the House welcomed me to my new home, explaining that everything in the house was now mine to enjoy. This was the house that grace had built, and faith was the key.

Surveying my new surroundings, I saw that the House of Salvation was a house with many rooms and I was only in the foyer. Across the way was a door marked Answered Prayer. Next to it was another that said, Daily Victory, and next to it, Every Need Supplied. The row of doors, each promising some spiritual blessing, stretched endlessly throughout the house.

The discovery of these other rooms puzzled me, for I failed to mention that the foyer in which I stood was jammed with people. It seemed that everyone who entered the house stopped in the foyer, never advancing beyond it, as though the foyer were the entire building.

This was little better than the highway. Couldn't they see that there was more to the House of Salvation than the foyer? Surely the Builder intended every room to be occupied. Hadn't He said that everything in the house was ours to enjoy? I, for one, had no desire to spend my life standing in a foyer. This was my Father's house; I was His child, and all He possessed was mine.

I went to the door marked Answered Prayer, grabbed the knob, and twisted. It was locked. I went to the next door, and the next, and the next. All were locked. But this time I didn't try to pick the lock or knock the door down. I remembered my encounter with the front door and knew you had to have a key.

Although I had been in the house only a short time, I had somehow managed to accumulate a large number of keys. Rummaging through my collection, I selected one tagged Doing Your Best, and tried it.

It didn't fit. Nor did the key of Religious Activity. The key of Sincerity proved useless. Next I tried the key of Tithing (I was getting desperate); but it was as powerless as the others. I was beginning to understand why the foyer was so crowded.

And then I heard a familiar voice. It was the Builder of the House. 'Child,' He said, 'do you remember the key I gave you to enter My house?'

'Yes, I remember.'

'What was it?'

'Why, it was the key of Faith,' I answered.

'The key of Faith,' He said, 'is a master key that unlocks every door in the house.

That was the greatest discovery of my life. Faith is the master key of the Christian life. From start to finish, salvation is a 'by grace through faith' operation. Everything we get in the Christian life we get by grace through faith. Grace makes it available and faith accepts it. Grace is God's hand giving; faith is man's hand receiving. Faith possesses what grace provides. Grace is God's part; faith is man's part. It is our positive response to God's gracious offer. Everything God demands of man can be summed up in one word: faith.

> Faith is the grasping of Almighty power;
> The hand of man laid on the arm of God;
> The grand and blessed hour
> In which things impossible to me
> Become possible, O Lord, through Thee.
>   *Anna E. Hamilton*

Faith is the identifying mark of the Christian. In early Christianity it was the primary word used to describe our relationship to God; we were called 'believers' before we were called Christians. To believe is our chief duty and the fountain from which all other duties flow. 'This is the work of God,' said Jesus, 'that you believe in Him whom He has sent' (John 6:29).

The Bible indicts unbelief as the supreme evil and the source of all other evils. It was unbelief that led Eve to succumb to the devil's tempting voice in the garden. Unbelief locked the doors of the Promised Land against Israel and sent her wandering in the desert for forty years. Men are lost, not because they lie and steal, but because they refuse to believe (John 3:18). Unbelief tied the hands of Jesus in His hometown and robbed many needy people of His gracious help.

The Just Shall Live By Faith

Four times the Bible declares, 'The just shall live by faith' (Habakkuk 2:4; Romans 1:17; Galatians 3:11; Hebrews 10:38, AV). When God says the same thing four times I get the idea He is trying to tell us something. And He is. He is trying to tell us that 'the just shall live by faith.' Note the word *live*. Not only are we saved through faith; we *live* by faith. Salvation commences with faith and continues the same way; we live the life the way we entered it. Faith is the pediatrician as well as the obstetrician. To the

Corinthians Paul said, 'We walk by faith' (2 Corinthians 5:7), and his personal testimony is recorded in Galatians 2:20: 'The life which I now live in the flesh I live by faith in the Son of God.'

Success in the Christian life is measured by faith. Always the word of Jesus is, '*Be it to you* according to your faith' (Matthew 9:29). All our failures are failures in faith.

It is by faith that we please God. 'Without faith it is impossible to please Him' (Hebrews 11:6). The writer doesn't say without faith it is difficult to please God–it is impossible.

It is by faith that the things possible to God become possible to man. 'With God all things are possible' (Matthew 19:26). 'All things are possible to him who believes' (Mark 9:23).

It is by faith that we overcome the world. 'And this is the victory that has overcome the world–our faith' (1 John 5:4).

It is by faith that we resist the devil. 'But resist him [the devil], firm in your faith' (1 Peter 5:9).

It is by faith that we conquer the problems of life. 'Truly I say to you, whoever says to this mountain, "Be taken up and cast into the sea,' and does not doubt in his heart, but believes that what he says is going to happen, it shall be granted him" ' (Mark 11:23).

It is by faith that we are made secure. 'Who are protected by the power of God through faith for a salvation ready to be revealed in the last time' (1 Peter 1:5). After predicting Peter's sifting by Satan,

Jesus assured the imperilled disciple that He had already prayed for him, that 'your faith may not fail' (Luke 22:32). Peter could survive the sifting if his courage and zeal failed—even if his love for Jesus failed; but not if his faith failed. His faith was crucial; if that went, everything was lost.

It is by faith that we receive all God has promised us. 'And everything you ask in prayer, believing, you shall receive' (Matthew 21:22). James 1:6, 7 says, 'But let him ask in faith without any doubting, for the one who doubts is like the surf of the sea driven and tossed by the wind. For let not that man expect that he will receive anything from the Lord.' Faith is the channel through which all that God has promised becomes ours. Through faith the blessings promised become the blessings possessed. Listen to these exciting words from Hebrews:

> And what more shall I say? For time will fail me if I tell of Gideon, Barak, Samson, Jephthah, of David and Samuel and the prophets, who by faith conquered kingdoms, performed acts of righteousness, obtained promises, shut the mouths of lions, quenched the power of fire, escaped the edge of the sword, from weakness were made strong, became mighty in war, put foreign armies to flight (Hebrews 11:32-34).

Neither God nor His methods have changed since those words were penned. There is no new way of obtaining the promises; the law of the Christian life is still, 'By faith.'

What Is It?

The Greek word for faith, also translated *belief* and *trust*, means 'the leaning of the entire human personality upon God or the Messiah in absolute trust and confidence in His power, wisdom and goodness.'[1] Contained in the word is the idea of *intellectual conviction*. Faith, then, is primarily an activity of the mind and the will. Contrary to popular notions, there is little or no emotion involved in biblical faith. Having been intellectually convinced and firmly persuaded, we commit ourselves totally to that of which we are convinced and persuaded. In the case of biblical faith, the basis of the conviction and commitment is God. And, as we will see in a later chapter, the convincer and persuader is the Holy Spirit.

The word faith has three basic uses in the Bible.

1. *The faith:* The whole body of Christian truth; the total revelation of God to man; the gospel message. This is its meaning in 2 Timothy 4:7, where Paul says, 'I have kept the faith,' and in Jude 3, '...contend earnestly for the faith.'

2. *Faith:* The act of believing, trusting, relying upon God. This is the most common use of the word and is the primary concern of this book.

3. *Faithfulness:* The quality of trustworthiness and steadfastness. Paul's Colossian letter is addressed to 'the faithful brethren in Christ.' Paul was placed in

the ministry because the Lord 'considered me faithful' (1 Timothy 1:12). This quality is the result of the act of faith. God is faithful and trustworthy and we become like the God we trust. Lightfoot says that the Hebrew and Greek words for faith 'hover between two meanings: *trustfulness*, the frame of mind which relies on another; and *trustworthiness*, the frame of mind which can be relied upon.' He goes on to say that the one quality of heart carries the other with it, 'so that they who are trustful are trusty also; they who have faith in God are steadfast and immovable in the path of duty.'[2]

To summarize, faith is an *affirmation*. It is our 'Amen' to all God has revealed about Himself. We accept as true the facts God has disclosed in His Word.

Faith is an *act*. Not only do we believe all God has said, we obey all He commands. Our conviction leads to action. Hebrews 11 makes it clear that to believe God is to obey Him.

Faith is an *attitude*. As a result of our conviction about God and our commitment to Him, we accept His blueprint for our lives and, day by day, live in total dependence upon Him. Living by faith means believing that God is actively interested and involved in our daily existence. It means looking to Him for wisdom, guidance, and strength. This is the *rest of faith*, resting in His sufficiency moment by moment.

And it is this attitude of faith, this *resting* in Him, that God desires most. This is the goal toward which everything He does is directed; it is the result of the affirmation and act of faith. In Mark 4:40, when Jesus rebuked the disciples for their little faith, He was actually saying, 'Have you not yet come to a settled attitude of faith?' They had had plenty of evidence that Jesus was able and willing to protect them and provide their every need–more than enough to bring them to a 'settled attitude of faith.' 'Jesus aims to lead the disciples to such an abiding attitude of trust that the apparently dangerous can be faced with calmness.'[3]

What Is He Looking For?

When Jesus saw the faith of the centurion (Matthew 8:10), He said, 'Truly I say to you, I have not found such great faith with anyone in Israel.' Jesus was *looking* for faith. Throughout His earthly ministry He searched the hearts of men and women for faith. And when He returns He will still be looking for that faith, for He says in Luke 18:8, 'When the Son of Man comes, will He find faith on the earth?'

Faith is the essential commodity in the Christian life. It is not optional equipment, not a luxury item. Without it there can be no true spiritual life. To those who believe, nothing is impossible. And to those who believe not, everything is impossible. Samuel Chadwick said it well when he wrote:

Faith is enough. Faith is all God asks. Faith is all Jesus asks: 'Ye believe in God, believe also in me.' When the ruler of the synagogue was told that his daughter was dead, Jesus steadied his faith, saying, 'Fear not: only believe'; and when the distraught father of the demoniac boy cried out against his own despair, our Lord assured him that 'all...things are possible to him that believeth.' Without faith man can do nothing with God, and God can do nothing with man.[4]

Notes

1. Alexander Souter, *A Pocket Lexicon to the Greek New Testament* (Oxford: Clarendon Press, 1956), p. 203.
2. J. B. Lightfoot, taken from *The Epistle of St. Paul to the Galatians* (Grand Rapids: Zondervan Publishing House, 1962), pp. 154, 155. Used by permission of The Zondervan Corporation.
3. Herbert Henry Wernecke, *'Faith' in the New Testament* (Grand Rapids: Zondervan Publishing House, 1934), p. 32.
4. Samuel Chadwick, *The Path of Prayer* (London: Hodder and Stoughton, 1931), p. 65.

CHAPTER TWO

The Real Thing

I t wasn't until I started to pay for the few items I had dumped on the counter that I realized all I had was a hundred dollar note. I was in Ft. Collins, Colorado, speaking at a conference on the campus of Colorado State University, and the only money I had with me was this hundred dollar note.

With a clatter of bells and buzzes, the cash register announced the total of my purchase: $7.02. I nonchalantly laid the hundred dollar note on the counter.

'Don't you have anything smaller?' the clerk asked.

'I'm sorry,' I said. 'That's the smallest thing I have.' I saw no reason to tell him it was the *only* thing I had.

Now properly impressed, the assistant scooped up the note and, grasping both ends in his hands and stretching the note tight, held it up to the light. I knew what he was doing, of course. Checking to see that it was good.

Then he did something unexpected. Picking up a notepad, he began to rub the note vigorously back and forth against the white paper. And right before my eyes, the white paper turned green. The ink was coming off that hundred dollar note! The thing was counterfeit! Where in the world had I got that note? I couldn't remember. Here I was, a stranger in town, buying a mere seven dollars' worth of stuff with a hundred dollar note. A classic way to pass funny money. Who would believe I didn't know the thing was counterfeit? I could see the headlines: BAPTIST PREACHER BAGGED WITH BOGUS NOTE.

While I was frantically trying to think of a plausible story, the assistant stopped his rubbing, looked up, and smiled. 'Well, it's good,' he said.

'It is?'

'Yes,' he said, pointing to the green-stained paper. 'The real thing always rubs off.'

What a relief. And what a lesson. Because I was unfamiliar with the nature of genuine US Treasury notes, I thought I had a forged note. And that is one of the real problems facing Christians in this matter of faith. If we don't know the nature of genuine faith, we will be vulnerable to deception and disappointment.

The sales assistant, confronted with a hundred dollar note from a stranger, knew how to test it, knew how to determine its authenticity.

Could we do the same with faith? Faced with something claiming to be faith, would we know how to prove or disprove its claim? In this chapter and the next, we want to learn how to identify true faith. We will look at three basic characteristics by which biblical faith can be identified. Two of these we will discuss in this chapter, and the third in the following chapter.

Faith's Credentials: Its Object

True faith is authenticated by its object. 'Faith in *what*?' is the question. *Believe* is a transitive verb requiring an object. When I hear someone say, 'Just have faith,' or 'Only believe,' I want to ask, 'Faith in *what*? Only believe *what*?' You must believe something or someone. Faith must have an object. To many people, the important thing is to believe—*what* you believe is secondary. They have the notion that there is something mystical, magical in the mere act of believing, a sort of holy *shazam* that transforms simple mortals into Captain Marvels. But the truth is, faith itself has no power. It is not faith that moves mountains, it is God. This is not to deny that the exercise of believing is psychologically uplifting; but, biblically speaking, faith, as a mere human activity, possesses no virtue, holds no merit, contains no power.

The power of faith lies in its object; faith is only as valid as its object. The crucial thing is not faith, but the object of faith. You can believe with all your heart and soul and mind until you turn blue—but if your faith is aimed at the wrong object, you're wasting your time.

What is the proper object of faith? Jesus identifies it in Mark 11:22: 'Have faith in God.' The object of faith is God. Jesus didn't tell His disciples to 'have faith', but to 'have faith in God.' Our faith must be *in God*. It may seem beside the point to mention this because everyone knows it, right? We might be surprised to find that our faith is frequently placed in things other than God.

For example, one writer advises his readers to 'have faith in faith.' Sounds sensible, doesn't it? Almost sounds scriptural. But the Bible never tells us to put our faith in our faith. That is positive thinking, not biblical faith. I don't mean to criticize positive thinking, or possibility thinking, or a positive mental attitude, or any such philosophy. I don't like negative thinking and I think we would all be happier and healthier if we maintained a positive mental attitude. But positive thinking is not the same thing as biblical faith. Faith will give you a positive attitude; but a positive attitude is not necessarily faith.

I labour this point because we seem to have a tendency to put our faith in our faith. When suddenly we encounter a mountain blocking our path and know that only by faith can we overcome it, we whip out our faith, hoping it is big enough to do the job. We measure it, weigh it, size it up in every possible way. And more often than not, we arrive at the sad conclusion that our faith isn't big enough to handle the crisis. How many times have we lamented over the weakness of our faith, using it as an excuse for failure?

'If only I had more faith.'

'My faith is so small.'

'Pray for me that I'll have more faith.'

But the fact is that almost everyone who came to Jesus for help brought along a faith that was weak and imperfect. And yet in spite of their weak faith, Jesus miraculously met their need. Remember when the disciples were crossing the sea and a storm threatened to sink the boat? Jesus was asleep and the disciples ran to Him, crying, 'Teacher, do You not care that we are perishing?' (Mark 4:38). Jesus rebuked the raging sea, then rebuked the faithless disciples. He did still the storm, in spite of their weak faith. I wouldn't have been surprised had Jesus said, 'If your faith was stronger I would calm the sea, but because your faith is so weak, I'm going to let the boat sink.' After all, their faith wasn't strong enough to stop a ripple, much less subdue towering waves. What counted was not the size of their faith, but the sort—its quality rather than its quantity. Although their faith was almost nonexistent, it had the right object—Jesus. What little faith they were able to muster, they brought to Jesus. It was not faith in their faith that saved them; it was faith in Jesus.

Frankly, I don't have much faith in my faith; I'm too well acquainted with it. I agree with Spurgeon when he said:

Never make a Christ out of your faith, nor think of it as if it were the independent source of your salvation. Our life is found in 'looking unto Jesus' (Hebrews 12:2), not looking to our own faith. By faith all things become possible to us, yet the power is not in the faith but in the God upon whom faith relies.... The peace within the soul is not derived from the contemplation of our own faith, but it comes to us from Him who is our peace.... See, then, that the weakness of your faith will not destroy you. A trembling hand may receive a golden gift.[1]

'Faith in faith' is really faith in yourself, in your ability to think positively and maintain a positive mental attitude. This means our attention is concentrated upon ourselves rather than upon Christ. We are looking at our faith when we should be looking at Jesus.

The writer of Hebrews, after parading before our eyes the mighty heroes of faith, says, 'Fixing our eyes on Jesus, the author and perfector of faith' (Hebrews 12:2). *Fixing our eyes* is the translation of a Greek word that means literally, 'looking away from and unto.' As great as these men and women of faith were, our eyes are not to be fastened on them or their faith, but upon Jesus. We must look away from everything else, our faith included, and concentrate on Jesus alone. James McConkey writes:

True faith pays no attention whatever to itself. It centers all its gaze upon Christ.... When Satan cannot beguile us in any other way he gets us to scrutinizing our faith, instead of looking unto Christ.... That faith is the strongest

which pays no attention to itself.... Nothing
will quicker weaken faith than the constant
endeavor to discover it. It is like a child's
digging up a seed to see if it's growing. It is a
curiosity which brings disaster to the seed....
Therefore do not worry about your faith....
Take care that you are depending upon
Jesus...and faith will take care of itself.[2]

Don't look at your faith, look at Jesus. Instead of
measuring your faith, measure your God. Rather
than evaluating a situation on the basis of your faith,
evaluate it on the basis of God's ability. Is God
capable? Is He big enough to handle your problems?
Who needs to ask? Of course, He is. Then commit
the situation to Him and trust Him to handle it.
That's what faith is–resting on God's faithfulness.

'But,' you say, 'my faith is so weak.' Yes, but your
God is so strong. Which are you going to trust–your
weak faith or your strong God?

A few years ago my family and some friends from
our church spent a few days' holiday in Colorado. It
was early March and winter still had an icy grip on
everything. Near the place we stayed were twelve
little trout lakes covered with ice. One day one of my
friends suggested I walk across one of the frozen
lakes, assuring me it was perfectly safe to do so since
they ice-skated on the lakes all through the winter.
I've lived in the South and Southwest all my life, and
the lakes there don't freeze solidly enough (if they
freeze at all) to support the weight of a child, much

less that of an adult. I promptly relayed these critical facts to my friend and respectfully declined his gracious offer.

Laughing, he said, 'Come on, Pastor. It's safe. And it may be your only chance to walk on the water.'

I still wasn't crazy about the idea, but after more coaxing, I ventured out. Perhaps ventured 'out' is stretching it. I inched my way out not more than a couple of yards from the shore because, unlike Peter, I doubted Jesus would reach out and save me if I began to sink. I kept a nervous eye on the shore and one on the ice, watching for cracks. And I tiptoed, because you weigh less when you tiptoe. You didn't know that?

Anyway, after a brief and nervous walk on the water, I scrambled back to the solid safety of the shore. I had little faith in the ice.

Later, as we drove back to our lodge, we passed another of the trout lakes and as I looked out the car window I saw a man sitting in the middle of the frozen lake. He was sitting on a wooden crate, hunched over a hole in the ice, fishing! I did a double take at that, feeling foolish as I recalled my timid excursion on the ice.

Now to the point: The man sitting in the middle of the frozen lake had great faith in the ice–right? I had almost no faith at all in the ice. Now which one of us was the safest? He with his great faith, or me with my little faith? Surely the man with the great faith was more secure. The fact is, the man with the great faith was no safer than I was with my little faith. Though my faith was practically nonexistent, I was just as safe as the fisherman who possessed great faith.

Why? It wasn't our faith that held us up. It was the ice. If it had been our faith supporting us, I would have sunk immediately. But I, with my little faith, was just as safe as the fisherman with his great faith.

What, then, is the advantage of having a great faith?

I'm glad you asked. Picture me on the ice: timid, nervous, afraid to venture out, constantly looking for cracks in the ice, fearing that at any moment the ice is going to betray me to the icy water beneath. Know any Christians like that? Timid, nervous, afraid to venture out on the Word of God, their eyes constantly searching for cracks in His promises, fearing that God may at any moment abandon them. There is no joy or excitement in their walk. That is the life of little faith.

Picture the fisherman: unafraid to step out on the ice, boldly venturing to the very middle, enjoying himself, resting his entire weight on the ice. You have seen a few Christians like that; they boldly step out on the promises of God, unafraid in the middle of His will, filled with joy and satisfaction, resting on the Word of God who cannot lie. That's the life of great faith.

As we drove past, I said, 'I wonder where he got enough nerve to do that.'

The driver answered immediately, 'Oh, he lives around here. He knows the ice.'

He knows the ice. And that is the difference between faith and no faith, weak faith and strong faith. The Psalmist said, 'And those who know Thy name will put their trust in Thee' (Psalm 9:10). And in Daniel's prophecy we read, '...the people who know their God will display strength and take action' (Daniel 11:32).

True faith is authenticated by its object, and the only valid object is God. The secret of faith is knowing God; and the greater our knowledge of Him and His Word, the greater will be our faith.

As Good As His Word

In saying that God is the sole object of faith, I include also His Word and His promises. Faith in God and faith in God's Word add up to the same thing. Behind a person's promise stands the person himself; and we believe his word only to the degree that we believe in him. You can't have faith in God's Word without having faith in the God who spoke it. And if we trust Him we will surely believe what He says to us.

When God gave Abraham the promises concerning his seed, the Bible says, 'Then he believed in the Lord' (Genesis 15:6). Abraham's faith in God's promise is described as faith in the Lord. And you remember Paul's stormy voyage to Rome. When all hope of survival was swept away by the rampaging sea, Paul stood in the midst of the terror-stricken passengers and declared that God had spoken to him through an angelic messenger, promising that 'there shall be no loss of life among you, but only of the ship' (Acts 27:22). And then the apostle, planted firmly on the promise of God, said, 'Therefore, keep up your courage, men, for I believe God, that it will turn out exactly as I have been told' (Acts 27:25). Behind the Word of God stood the character of God, and that was good enough for Paul. For him, faith in God and faith in His Word were the same.

G. D. Watson said, 'Our limitless trust in God seems to satisfy Him as nothing else can do, because it corresponds with His eternal faithfulness, it honours His veracity, and it is a constant silent worship of all His perfections.'[3]

Faith's Credentials: Its Objective

Throughout this volume we will again and again hammer at this fact: genuine faith is born out of a knowledge of the will of God and exists only to fulfil that will. The objective of faith is the will of God. Faith is not a means of getting man's will done in heaven; it is the means of getting God's will done on earth. Faith does not put God at our beck and call; rather it puts us at His. It is for 'official use only', and is operational only within the sphere of His will.

This is probably the hardest thing to learn about faith; and to learn it well, two things are necessary.

1. *We must accept the will of God as the best thing that can happen.* More than to accept it as the best thing, we need to believe, really believe, that it *is* the

best thing that can happen, for it is. And, I suppose, we have to take even this by faith. For there are times when, to our sight and senses, the will of God appears to be less than the best. I remember one trying experience in my life when I had no doubt that what I was doing was the will of God–yet it was one of the most painful times of my life. I told some friends, 'I don't see how anything this miserable could be the will of God.' But it was, and the misery was only temporary.

When Paul describes the will of God as 'that which is good and acceptable and perfect' (Romans 12:2), he means that the will of God in and of itself is good. It is intrinsically good. Nothing needs to be added to it to make it good. In other words, it is not the will of God plus a good job that is good, or the will of God plus my prayers answered that is good, or the will of God plus my baby being healed that is good. It is not the will of God *plus* anything; the will of God is good alone, all by itself.

To believe that God loves us is to be delivered from the fear of what He might do to us or withhold from us, for 'no good thing does He withhold from those who walk uprightly' (Psalm 84:11). Like our Lord, we must learn to say, 'My food is to do the will of Him who sent Me' (John 4:34).

2. *We must let the Bible say what it wants to say.* By this I mean we must refuse to manipulate the Word of God and must let it speak for itself. I think I can best illustrate this with an incident that occurred

several years ago. I was conducting a Bible conference in Houston, Texas, and a friend I had not
seen in four or five years dropped by the church. He
explained that he was just passing through and
happened to see the advertisements for the meeting
in the newspaper. As we visited I learned that he had
come by some new beliefs since I had last seen him.
One of them was the belief that all sickness was of
the devil and that it was always God's will for everyone to be healed. He quoted Matthew 4:23: 'And
Jesus was going about in all Galilee, teaching in their
synagogues, and proclaiming the gospel of the kingdom, and healing every kind of disease and every
kind of sickness among the people.' And then he
quoted 1 Peter 2:24: 'And He Himself bore our sins
in His body on the cross, that we might die to sin and
live to righteousness; for by His wounds you were
healed.'

I didn't want to get into an argument about divine
healing, but I did feel I should point out something
to my friend. 'When you get back to your room,' I
told him, 'I'd like you to read those two passages
again, and I think you will see that the verse in
Matthew is speaking only of what Jesus did during
His public ministry on earth. Nothing is said about
Jesus continuing that ministry after ascending to
heaven. And the verse in Peter–if you study the
context, it's obvious that Peter is talking about spiritual healing from our sins, not physical healing.'

He returned the next day and said, 'Well, I did

what you asked. And you were right about both those verses.'

I felt good; I had a convert.

Then he said, 'Now I've got to find some new verses.'

See the point? He had already made up his mind what he believed and he had to find some verses to try to support it. That's why we fall prey to manipulating the Bible to make it say what we want it to say.

The bottom line of all this is, if I believe the will of God is always best, then I will be satisfied to let the Bible speak for itself.

The third identifying credential of real faith is its origin. This will be discussed in the following chapter.

Notes

1. C. H. Spurgeon, *All of Grace* (Chicago: Moody Press, n.d.), p. 44.
2. James McConkey, *Give God a Chance* (Chicago: Moody Press, 1975), p. 19.
3. Edwin and Lillian Harvey, *Kneeling We Triumph* (Chicago: Moody Press, 1974), p. 37.

CHAPTER THREE

The Origin of Faith

S ome time ago I received a letter from a man defending a questionable doctrinal position. He wrote: 'I don't know the Bible or theology, but I have faith.' He seemed to be saying that whatever difficulties existed with his position were overcome by the fact that he had faith. The bottom line was not, 'What does the Bible say?' but 'Do I have faith?'

I don't doubt for a minute that he had faith. We all do. But what kind of faith? Faith is standard equipment in human beings; it is native to our nature. We live by faith, exercising it a hundred different ways every day. We sit in a chair by faith, believing it will support our weight. When we board an aeroplane we are placing our faith in the plane and the pilot. Our doctor tell us we have a disease we've never heard of, writes a prescription we can't read for a medicine whose name we can't pronounce, which we take to a chemist we don't know, who gives us a bottle of liquid that tastes like poison which we take and go back for more—that's faith.

But we do not commit ourselves to Christ with the same kind of faith we use to sit in a chair. A chair we can measure with our physical senses; Christ we cannot. While God has given to every man the capacity to believe, biblical faith is more than simply transferring our natural faith to spiritual objects. Just as a man's spirit must be reborn before he can fellowship with God, and his mind renewed before he can think after God, so his capacity to believe must be quickened before he can have faith in God.

Natural faith and biblical faith operate the same way, but in different realms. Take, for example, an AM radio and an FM radio. They function in the same manner: you plug them in, switch on, rotate the dial, and pick up a station. But you can't tune in an FM programme with an AM radio. They operate the same way, but in different spheres. And natural faith cannot operate in the spiritual realm.

Where Does Faith Come From?

In the last chapter we discussed two of faith's credentials. Now we come to the third, the origin of faith. Faith's origin is revealed by Paul in Romans 10:17: 'So faith comes from hearing, and hearing by the word of Christ.'

Faith *comes*. If a man has faith (from this point on when I speak of faith, I mean biblical faith), it had to come to him from an outside source. It did not originate within himself. Unlike natural faith, biblical faith is not native to man. Natural faith is inherent in man; biblical faith is imparted by God. A person may be born with a silver spoon in his mouth, but never with the key of faith in his pocket.

We do not generate faith or work it up. Faith is

not convincing ourselves that something is true. When someone says, 'I just can't believe,' he usually means he is unable to convince himself that a thing is so.

A few years ago I had a terrific battle with insomnia. After several months of sleepless nights I went to the doctor for a checkup. When the tests were complete he told me there was nothing physically wrong with me. He even told me I was not overweight. This surprised me, because I thought I was.

'You're too short,' he said. 'According to this chart you should be seven feet three inches tall.'

Not only did my doctor crack jokes, he also refused to prescribe sleeping pills. But he said there was something he could do to help. He wanted to teach me self-hypnosis. This way, he said, I could put myself to sleep whenever I wanted and would awaken without a drug hangover. To be honest, I was reluctant. Something about hypnosis disturbed me. The word conjured up the picture of a nightclub magician in tails and top hat making people cluck like chickens and bark like dogs. But he assured me it was absolutely safe and perfectly natural, and that he had had great success with it in many patients. So I agreed to the six weekly sessions he required.

It was a great disappointment. Not because it didn't work—it did. But it was so utterly simple. Thinking I was to be initiated into some deep, dark mysterious secret, I learned that self-hypnosis is nothing more than talking yourself into going to sleep. You concentrate on an object such as a grease spot on the wall or a dead fly on the window ledge, and start telling yourself over and over that you are sleepy. After a while your mind begins to believe what you're telling it and, bingo, you're asleep. It's simply mind over mattress.

And to many Christians, faith is a form of self-hypnosis. They try to talk themselves into believing, sort of psyching themselves up to a point where they believe, and then they hurriedly pray 'before it melts'.

But faith is not generated by us; it is given by God. It originates with Him; He initiates faith and imparts it to us. In 2 Peter 1:1, it says, 'Simon Peter, a bond-servant and apostle of Jesus Christ, to those who have received a faith of the same kind as ours.' And in Ephesians 2:8, we read: 'For by grace you have been saved through faith; and that not of yourselves, it is the gift of God.' From start to finish, salvation is a work of God. Everything involved in the saving of an individual originates with God, even the faith to receive His grace. In Philippians 1:29, Paul writes, 'For to you it has been granted for Christ's sake, not only to believe in Him, but also to suffer for His sake.'

Our faith does not depend upon our ability to believe, but upon His ability to impart it to us.

I stated earlier that natural faith and biblical faith are different, that biblical faith is more than taking the same faith we exercise in daily living and applying it to spiritual things. No one can believe God unless God enables him. This is made clear by the words of Jesus to the unconverted Jews of His day.

But though He had performed so many signs before them, yet they were not believing in Him; that the word of Isaiah the prophet might be fulfilled, which he spoke, 'LORD, WHO HAS BELIEVED OUR REPORT? AND TO WHOM HAS THE ARM OF THE LORD BEEN REVEALED?' For this cause they could not believe, for Isaiah said again, 'HE HAS BLINDED THEIR EYES, AND HE HARDENED THEIR HEART; LEST THEY SEE WITH THEIR EYES, AND PERCEIVE WITH THEIR HEART, AND BE CONVERTED, AND I HEAL THEM' (John 12:37-40).

Here is a striking example of men who *could not believe* because God refused to enable them to believe.

A similar incident is recorded in John 8:47: 'He who is of God hears the words of God; for this reason you do not hear them, because you are not of God.' These people could hear what Jesus was saying; they had ears and a natural ability to hear. But one does not hear the voice of God with physical ears and natural ability. Unless God imparts the spiritual ability to hear His voice, one hears nothing but meaningless words. We do not hear God with natural ears, nor do we believe Him with natural faith.

The Credit Goes To God

The focus of our concern should not be upon our inability to believe, but upon God's ability to enable us to believe. When the conditions are right (we will discuss the conditions later in this chapter), God will impart to us all the faith we need to trust Him in a given situation. It is a fundamental tenet of grace that whatever God demands, God provides.

When my brother and I were small boys we would go to our father at Christmas time and ask for money so we could buy him a present. Dad would give us a few dollars and we would go to town and buy him a Christmas present with his own money. On Christmas morning under the tree would be a gift with a card that read: 'To Dad from Barry and Ronnie.' It didn't occur to me how presumptuous that was–buying my father a present with his own money and then acting as though the gift came from me. It didn't occur to me until my children came to me at Christmas time asking for money so they could buy me a present.

It is the same with the faith we bring to God. We are simply presenting to Him that which He has given us. This means that whenever God puts us in a situation that demands faith we can be assured that He will provide the faith He demands. And He will never demand more than He has provided.

In this way God gets all the credit for any faith we may have; and thus, 'no flesh can glory in His presence.'

How God Imparts Faith

'Faith comes by hearing', says Paul, 'and hearing by the word of Christ'. The instrument God uses to impart faith is His word.

1. The External Word. One of the most common misconceptions about faith is that it is a substitute for knowledge. One dictionary defines faith as 'believing without evidence'. As one child put it: 'Faith is believing things you're not sure of.' When we are uncertain about a person or a fact then we must 'take it on faith.' In other words, faith takes up where facts leave off. This may be true of natural faith but not of biblical faith.

Biblical faith is founded on facts—facts found in the Word of God. Faith begins with a knowledge of God's Word, without which there can be no genuine faith. I've heard people say, 'If you believe with all your heart, you will get what you want.' But this kind of faith is based on our own desires or sense of need. It originates within ourselves and depends upon our own ability to believe; it is religious self-hypnosis. This is the kind of faith the man had who wrote, 'I don't know the Bible, but I have faith.' To him faith was a substitute for knowledge, a compensation for ignorance. Some even brag about their ignorance and glory in it as though it were a requirement for faith. To them knowledge is a barrier to believing and faith is a leap into the dark.

But faith is a leap into the light, the light of God's Word. Without this light we cannot exercise faith in

God. Reduced to its simplest form, faith is *man's positive response to divine revelation*. It is action based on knowledge. Dr Curtis Mitchell says:

> In order to exercise biblical faith you have to have facts from God. You must have a Word from God on the matter. Otherwise you have no basis for biblical faith. Faith is founded on the Word of God. If you don't have a Word from God on the matter, then you are not in a position to exercise faith.[1]

Hebrews 11:1 defintes faith as 'the assurance of things hoped for, the conviction of things not seen.' The phrase 'things hoped for' can be confusing if we don't understand the biblical use of the word 'hope'. To us *hope* implies uncertainty; it is a wishing, a maybe, a perhaps. But there is not a trace of uncertainty in the biblical word. In the Bible, hope is based on divine promises. It is a word of assurance that we will receive what God has promised. The only uncertainty associated with biblical hope is the time of its fulfilment. The 'things hoped for' are the things God has promised. If God has not promised them, all the believing in the world will not obtain them.

To discover what God has promised we must go to His Word. Ignorance of or indifference to the Bible results in little or no faith. The instances of imperfect faith recorded in the Gospels were directly related to imperfect understanding of the divine revelation.

Look, for example, at the feeding of the five thousand. After the multitude had eaten, Jesus commanded His disciples to gather up the remaining food, which amounted to twelve baskets full. When this was done, He told them to get into a boat and make their way to Bethsaida. He would join them later. And join them He did—walking on the water. When the disciples saw Him they thought it was a ghost and were terrified. Then followed Peter's brief walk on the water. When he began to sink he cried out in fear. The Lord grabbed him and said, 'O you of little faith, why did you doubt?' (Matthew 14:31). Mark's account ends with this explanation of their faithless fear: 'For they did not understand the lesson of the loaves; their minds were dull' (Mark 6:52, Williams Translation).[2]

Loaves? What did bread have to do with boats? What did the feeding of the five thousand have to do with walking on the water? Their failure to understand the miracle of the loaves affected their behaviour in the boat. Remember that the disciples gathered up twelve baskets of divinely produced food—that's one basket full for each disciple. Then they immediately boarded the boat, taking the baskets of food with them. Each disciple had at his feet the tangible evidence of the power of Jesus to provide and preserve, a basket filled with miraculously baked loaves. But they failed 'to gain any insight' from that miracle. The lesson of the loaves was that Jesus is quite able to handle any situation that might arise. It demonstrated His power over all creation and, even more important, His compassionate concern for His followers. But the disciples failed to understand.

Still later the disciples again had a problem with boats and bread. Isn't it strange how we keep stumbling over the same problems? But the Lord continues to give us the exam until we pass. This time Jesus and His disciples take a boat to the region of Magadan. When they arrive the disciples realize they have forgotten to bring bread. At the same moment they make their discovery, Jesus warns them of the leaven of the Pharisees and Sadducees. The disciples interpret His words as a rebuke for forgetting the bread.

> But Jesus, aware of this, said, 'You men of little faith, why do you discuss among yourselves because you have no bread? Do you not yet understand or remember the five loaves of the five thousand, and how many large baskets you took up?... How is it that you do not understand that I did not speak to you concerning bread...?' (Matthew 16:8, 9, 11).

Do you not yet understand? Their little faith was caused by their lack of understanding. A person does not have little faith because he has little willpower to believe, but because he has little understanding of the Word and will of God. Our ability to believe is measured by our understanding of the Lord and His Word. The centurion in Matthew 8 had such great faith that Jesus marvelled at it; but the source of his great faith was in his understanding of Jesus and His mission.

In his book, *Evangelism in a Tangled World*, Wayne McDill writes:

> The strength or weakness of our faith is directly related to the accuracy of our knowledge and understanding of the nature and purpose of God. Our faith depends on knowing something factual about God.... Faith, then, is not reaching out to the unknown, unbelievable, unseen possibilities beyond our own understanding. Faith is rather, in the biblical view, a response on our part to a clear word from God.[2]

2. The Internal Word. But faith requires more than an intellectual knowledge of the Word of God; for while we cannot have faith without knowing the Bible, it's possible to know the Bible without having faith. I know of a minister who worries himself sick over every little problem that comes along. One day as he was fretting and fussing over a minor difficulty, one of his associates said, 'Pastor, why don't you just turn this over to the Lord and trust Him to handle it?' Unhinged, the pastor said, 'I've never learned to do that!' This wouldn't merit mentioning were it not for the fact that I have heard this man preach several times about living by faith. It is possible to be a Bible scholar and at the same time not realize what it means to trust God in everyday living.

The impartation of faith requires more than intellectual knowledge of the Word. Let's take another look at Romans 10:17: 'So faith comes from hearing, and hearing by the word of Christ.' We're going to have to drill through some grammatical rock to get to the water to understand Paul's meaning. Throughout the New Testament two different words are used for 'the word of God.' The most frequent is the familiar word *logos*, meaning the expression of a thought, a message, a discourse. When referring to the Word of God, it means the total revelation of God, all that God has spoken to man, the gospel message. For instance, Jesus is called the Word (*logos*) of God in John 1:1 because He is the full and complete revelation of God to man.

The other word is *rhema*. This is a spoken word, an utterance, the concrete expression of *logos*.[3] *Rhema* is someone speaking, uttering.

Logis is the Word; *rhema* is a word from the Word. *Logos* is the message; *rhema* is the message spoken. *Logis* is the content of the message; *rhema* is the communication of that message. In *logos* the emphasis is on substance; in *rhema* the emphasis is on sound. *Logos* is the entire Bible; *rhema* is a verse from the Bible.

Commenting on the phrase, 'the sword of the Spirit, which is the word [*rhema*] of God,' in Ephesians 6:17, W. E. Vine says:

The significance of *rhema* (as distinct from *logos*) is exemplified in the injunction to take

'the sword of the Spirit, which is the word of
God' (Ephesians 6:17); here the reference is
not to the whole Bible as such, but to the individual Scripture which the Holy Spirit brings to
our remembrance for us in time of need, a
prerequisite being the regular storing of the
mind with Scripture.[4]

A word of caution, however. We must not in
every instance make too much of the distinction
between these two words, for they are used inter-
changeably in the New Testament. The context must
determine when the distinction is made, as we are
about to see.

The word Paul uses in Romans 10:17 is *rhema*.
Some translations read 'the message of Christ' and
give the impression that Paul is referring to the message about Christ that the preacher delivers. If Paul
had used *logos* there would be no doubt that he was
referring to the message about Christ; but the use of
rhema suggests something more.

In this context, *rhema* can be translated *utterance*:
'and hearing by the utterance of Christ.' I believe the
reference is not to the preacher's message about
Christ, but *the actual utterance of Christ Himself*. In
this tenth chapter of Romans, Paul makes a careful
distinction between preaching and hearing. There
must be preaching, but it is not preaching that produces faith; it is hearing. And the hearing to which
he refers is not the hearing of the preacher's message, but rather of the utterance of Christ—the voice

of Christ speaking through the message the preacher delivers. A person may hear clearly the preacher's utterance about Christ; but unless he also hears the accompanying utterance of Christ to his heart, there will be no faith.

This harmonizes with what Paul says in verse 14 of this same chapter. The Authorised Version reads, 'How then shall they call on him in whom they have not believed? and how shall they believe in him of whom they have not heard? and how shall they hear without a preacher?'

The phrase, 'how shall they believe in him of whom they have not heard?' is more accurately translated in the New American Standard Bible as, 'how shall they believe in Him whom [not *of* whom] they have not heard?' There is a great difference in hearing *about* or *of* someone and actually *hearing* someone. Dr Curtis Vaughan says, 'There is a close connection here between the proclaimed word and the presence of Christ.'[5] Paul is saying that if men are to believe they must hear Christ Himself.

The thought that Christ Himself speaks to us is also brought out in Ephesians 2:17: 'And He came and preached peace to you who were far away, and peace to those who were near.' And again in Ephesians 4:20, 21: 'But you did not learn Christ in this way, if indeed you have heard Him and have been taught in Him, just as truth is in Jesus.'

The Fact Becomes A Force

All this means that there must be a spiritual hearing as well as a physical hearing, a quickening of our spirit by His Spirit that enables us to perceive the voice of Christ speaking to us through His Word. Without this divine quickening we will hear the words of the preacher but not the Word of God and, thus, be unable to act in faith on what we have heard. We may know what the Bible teaches about trusting Christ but we will have to confess, 'I've never learned to do that.'

Before there can be faith, divine enlightenment and enablement are required. Speaking of the condition of the lost, Paul says in 2 Corinthians 4:4, 'In whose case the god of this world has blinded the minds of the unbelieving, that they might not see the light of the gospel of the glory of Christ, who is the image of God.' He goes on to say that it is God who shines the light into our eyes that we may believe. No man can create his own light nor remove the blindfold from his eyes. That is accomplished by God alone.

But this divine enlightenment is needed by Christians as well. For the Ephesian believers Paul prayed, 'that the God of our Lord Jesus Christ ... may give you a spirit of wisdom and of revelation in the knowledge of Him ... that the eyes of your heart may be enlightened, so that you may know what is the hope of His calling.' A divine revelation to their hearts was required before the

Ephesians could know and appreciate what they had in Christ.

Faith requires a personal encounter with the living Christ. When the woman of Samaria who met Jesus at Jacob's well rushed back to town with the news that she had found the Messiah, the men of the city went to see for themselves. After their encounter with Christ they said to the woman, 'It is no longer because of what you said that we believe, for we have heard for ourselves and know that this One is indeed the Saviour of the world' (John 4:42).

After the resurrection, the disciples found it difficult to believe the reports of Christ's resurrection. They were convinced only after a personal encounter with Him. It took the resurrected Christ to assure them that He was indeed alive.

Our relationship to Christ is more than intellectual—it is personal and spiritual. It is not enough to hear or read the Bible. Christ must do for us what He did for the two disciples on the road to Emmaus: 'And beginning with Moses and with all the prophets, He explained to them the things concerning Himself in all the Scriptures' (Luke 24:27). The word translated 'explained' means 'to open completely.' Verse 31 says, 'And their eyes were opened and they recognized Him.'

Doesn't that strike you as strange? These men had accompanied Jesus for three-and-a-half years and yet they did not recognize Him until 'their eyes were opened.' They saw Him with their natural eyes; but recognition and belief came only when Christ

enabled them to see with their spiritual eyes. Later
in the same chapter we find Jesus speaking to the
disciples concerning the things written of Him in the
Scriptures. Verse 45 states, 'Then He opened their
minds to understand the Scriptures.'

All this is to say that it takes more than an intellectual understanding of the Bible to produce faith.
Thomas Aquinas said, 'It is God who causes faith in
the believer by prompting his will and enlightening
his intellect.' The Holy Spirit must illumine what He
has inspired. As we hear the Word of God, Christ
speaks to us through His Spirit, making the Word
real to our hearts. The Word comes alive; the fact
becomes a force. It is as though, while we are listening to the preacher, Christ whispers 'Amen' to our
hearts, giving an inner confirmation to what we are
hearing. Only then are we able to grasp with the
strong arm of faith the promise of God and appropriate all His grace has made available.

How To Hear

While faith is initiated and imparted by God, man is
responsible for believing and is held accountable for
any lack of faith. If we believe, it is because God
enabled us; but if we do not believe, it is our own
fault.

Israel heard but did not believe. The fault was
theirs alone and God held them liable for their
unbelief. Why did they not believe? In Romans 10
Paul states that faith comes by hearing; then he

immediately says that Israel heard but did not believe. If hearing produces faith, why didn't faith come to Israel when the nation heard? The explanation is given in verse 21, and in that explanation are found the human conditions necessary for hearing with faith.

'But as for Israel He says, "ALL DAY LONG I HAVE STRETCHED OUT MY HANDS TO A DISOBEDIENT AND OBSTINATE PEOPLE." '

Note the twofold description of Israel: disobedient and obstinate. 'Disobedient' refers to more than a simple, isolated act of disobedience. It indicates a stubborn refusal to obey, an unwillingness to be persuaded. Israel had made up its mind to disbelieve and disobey before it heard what God had to say.

'Obstinate' means to contradict what is said, to speak against it, to debate it.

Hearing did not produce faith in Israel because the nation (1) had already decided to disobey before it heard; and (2) Israel argued and debated what it heard. Turning these two negatives into positive attitudes, we conclude that if we are to hear with faith there must be (1) a readiness to obey, and (2) a willingness to listen.

1. A Readiness to Obey. I have been a minister for over twenty-five years, and most of my preaching has been to juries. You know what a jury is—it is a group of people who come together to listen to some facts, then go off and think about it for awhile. Then if the facts seem right and reasonable, they do something about it. And that's the way most of us listen to the Word of God. But God will not commit Himself to us on that kind of proposition. The Word of God is not on trial.

The proper attitude for hearing with faith is one that says, 'Lord, I don't know what You are going to say to me, but I commit myself to obey what You say even before You say it.' It is signing a blank contract and allowing God to fill in the terms.

'But I can't do that,' someone says. Why not? Are you afraid God will take advantage of you? Do you believe that once He has you in His clutches He will pull some dirty trick on you? Suppose my son said to me, 'Dad, from now on I'm going to do everything you tell me to do, without arguing about it or asking why.' What would my reaction be? Would I say to myself, 'Now I've got this kid right where I want him. Now, what's the dirtiest, meanest, lowest thing I can do to him?' Of course not. And if I, being evil, know how to give good things to my son, how much more does my heavenly Father?

A readiness to obey is the expression of our confidence in a loving heavenly Father. But we cannot expect God to reveal Himself to us if our attitude is, 'First, tell me what You want and then I'll decide whether to obey.' We must preface our hearing of the Word of God with a commitment to obey even before we know what it is He asks of us. That is a readiness to obey.

2. A Willingness to Listen. This is the correct order, for if we have decided not to obey, we are not going to listen willingly. A disobedient spirit makes hearing the Word impossible. But if we have settled the matter of obedience, we are eager to hear what God says.

This willingness to listen is what James referred to when he said, 'Receive with meekness the engrafted word' (James 1:21, AV). Meekness is having a *teachable spirit*. It is the attitude of a pupil before his teacher. The finest piano teacher in the world cannot help a student who debates and argues with everything the teacher says. A willingness to listen is listening with a view to obeying. We do not listen in order to weigh and evaluate what is said; we do not listen in order to offer suggestions or alternatives. We listen to obey.

We hear what we are prepared to hear. I have often assumed God wasn't speaking, when the fact was I was not hearing. The trouble was in the receiver, not the transmitter. It is God's responsibility to speak; ours to hear. It is God's responsibility to impart faith; ours to receive it. And God will impart to us all the faith we need if we are in the right position to receive it. You can depend on God to do His part. Our concern must be focused on our part–preparing our hearts to hear and receive. To those who are ready to obey and are willing to listen, God will speak. And we will hear–with faith. 'Speak, Lord, for Thy servant heareth.'

Notes

1. Curtis C. Mitchell, *Let's Live!* (Old Tappan, N.J.: Fleming H. Revell, 1975), p. 115.
2. Wayne McDill, *Evangelism in a Tangled World* (Nashville: Broadman Press, 1976), p. 87.
3. Alexander Souter, *A Pocket Lexicon to the Greek New Testament* (Oxford: Clarendon Press, 1956), p. 227.
4. W. E. Vine, *An Expository Dictionary of New Testament Words* (Old Tappan, N.J.: Fleming H. Revell, 1940), p. 230.
5. Curtis Vaughan and Bruce Corley, taken from *Romans, A Study Guide Commentary* (Grand Rapids: Zondervan Publishing House, 1976), p. 120. Copyright © 1967 by The Zondervan Corporation. Used by permission.

CHAPTER FOUR

Miracle, Anyone?

I have good news for you. There's nothing wrong with you that a miracle wouldn't cure.

Now, don't you feel better? And you thought you were a hopeless case.

If you're like most people, you are probably thinking, 'That's exactly what it will take–a miracle. And it will be a miracle if I get one.'

That's the trouble with miracles–never one around when you need it.

Don't be too sure. One may be closer than you think.

But then, you don't really expect a miracle, do you? I thought not.

Well, you're in good company. The Lord Jesus had a disciple just like you. His name was Peter. One day as Jesus and His disciples journeyed from Bethany to Jerusalem, they came to a fig tree. From a distance Jesus could see that the tree was heavily laden with leaves; and since leaves on those particular fig trees signalled fruit, He expected to find the tree loaded with fruit. But as He drew near He saw that the tree was barren. It was a hypocrite. By bearing leaves it was claiming to be fruitful; but it was false advertising. As a result, Jesus cursed it, saying, 'May no one ever eat fruit from you again'

(Mark 11:14). The next day as they returned to Bethany they passed the fig tree, now withered from the roots up. Peter, remembering what had happened the day before, was astonished and said to Jesus, 'Rabbi, behold, the fig tree which You cursed has withered' (Mark 11:21).

To Peter's exclamation, Jesus calmly replied, 'Have faith in God. Truly I say to you, whoever says to this mountain, "Be taken up and cast into the sea," and does not doubt in his heart, but believes that what he says is going to happen, it shall be granted him' (Mark 11:22, 23).

Jesus was saying, 'Peter, don't be surprised at the simple withering of a fig tree. That's nothing compared to what can happen if you have faith in God. Why, if you know how to believe God, you can command a mountain to jump into the sea and it will obey you.'

That this was Jesus' meaning is made clear by Matthew's account of the same incident: 'And Jesus answered and said to them, "Truly I say to you, if you have faith, and do not doubt, you shall not only do what was done to the fig tree, but even if you say to this mountain, 'Be taken up and cast into the sea,' it shall happen" ' (Matthew 21:21).

What a fantastic promise! Miracles at our command, mountains at our disposal. I would have been satisfied at withering fig trees, wouldn't you? But moving mountains.... And this shouldn't surprise us as though it were uncommon. Rather, it should be the norm, the ordinary, the expected. And the condition for fulfilling the promise is as amazing as the promise itself: 'Have faith in God.'

But, someone may ask, wasn't this some sort of dispensational promise limited to the original disciples? Two facts lead me to believe this promise is both eternal and universal in its application. First, the words preceding the promise, 'Truly I say to you,' are found throughout the Gospels and constitute a formula Jesus employed when enunciating a timeless truth.

Second, the promise says 'whoever'. Nothing in the verse or its context warrants limiting it to the first-century disciples. Consistency demands that we interpret this *whoever* as having the same timeless application as the *whoever* of John 3:16.

What Is A Miracle?

You probably won't find this definition in a theological textbook, but in my opinion it is accurate. A miracle is *God doing what only God can do*. It is a happening beyond man's power to produce or prevent. It is God moving that which cannot be moved, building that which cannot be built, destroying that which cannot be destroyed. This sovereign act of the Almighty may at times be spectacular and sensational; or at other times it may appear so ordinary that we fail to recognize it as a miraculous work of God. We declare with the authority of our ignorance, 'The day of miracles is past.' But the discerning eye of faith sees the hand of God in the 'natural' as well as in the supernatural.

There's no doubt about it—this promise would strain the faith of the strongest saint. Did Jesus say what He meant? Did He mean what He said? Is it possible, if we have enough faith, to cast a literal mountain of dirt, rocks, and trees into the sea? Could I, by the sheer power of faith, relocate Mt. Everest to the nearest ocean? Frankly, I don't think that is what Jesus had in mind. I think He meant something far greater!

Remember our definition of a miracle: God doing that which only God can do. Given enough time and equipment and dynamite, man can move a mountain into the sea. But we're talking about something only God can do. Furthermore, we have no record of either Jesus or any of His disciples doing such a thing. Casting a mountain into the sea would serve no redemptive purpose; and we must remember that Jesus was no side-show sensationalist. Everything He did had a redemptive purpose.

In the Bible mountains are used to symbolize barriers and hindrances. They represent immovable objects, insurmountable problems that block the path of God's people, making progress impossible. For instance, Isaiah the prophet speaks of the time when the people will be released from their captivity and return to their homeland. But standing between them and their destination are mountains, towering barricades shouting like Amalek, 'This is as far as you go.' Speaking through the prophet, God says,

'And I will make all My mountains a road...' (Isaiah 49:11). God promises to turn the mountains into a freeway; in other words, the mountains will be cast into the sea, leaving the path open and clear.

A mountain is anything that threatens to halt or hinder our God-appointed journey. It is anything that prevents us from doing what God has commanded, or becoming what God has promised. Jesus is telling us that if we can believe, there is nothing that can keep us from doing what God has commanded us to do or becoming what God has saved us to be. And that, dear friend, is good news.

An Amazing Promise: 'All Things Are Possible'

To the questioning father of the demon-possessed boy, Jesus said, 'All things are possible to him who believes' (Mark 9:23). Whatever obstacle stands between us and the will of God can be uprooted by the command of faith. Just think of it. There is nothing, absolutely nothing, that can keep us from doing the will of God–if we believe.

Behind the will of God is thrown the power of God. When God commands us to be or do something, He places at our disposal all the resources of heaven. And faith is the key that releases those resources into our situation. If I know God's will in a given circumstance, I can be assured that He stands ready to supply whatever is needed to accomplish that will.

Every Command A Promise

God never asks us to do anything that we cannot do. With the command comes the ability to obey. When Jesus stood before the grave of Lazarus He gave him an impossible command. 'Lazarus, come forth,' He ordered. But that is an impossible command. If Lazarus could come forth he would have done it before now. The Lord is asking too much: Lazarus can't come forth. But he does. For when Jesus issues the command He also imparts at the same time the power to obey.

One day Jesus met a man with a withered arm. 'Stretch forth thine hand,' Jesus said. But that is what is wrong with a withered hand—you can't stretch it forth. Yet he did. With the command came the power to obey the command. That makes every command a promise. If God commands us to do something, we know it is in fact a promise that can be fulfilled. No wonder the apostle John said that His commands are not burdensome (1 John 5:3). Our part, then, is to discover where God is going, join Him, and command the mountains to get out of the way.

An Aggressive, Authoritative Faith

This kind of faith launches an offensive attack against the mountains that oppose the will of God. Rather than a passive, arms-folded, 'there's-nothing-we-can-do-about-it' attitude, it is a shout that crumbles the walls of Jericho like dead leaves. It splits the waters of the Red Sea so we can escape the counter-attack of the enemy and march on toward the Promised Land. It refuses to accept the status quo when 'the status ain't nothing to quo about.'

Several years ago I spoke at a men's retreat in the beautiful Colorado mountains. We were experiencing an unusually blessed time; it was obvious God was moving in an extraordinary way in the lives of the 300 men present. As the men crowded into the chapel on the last night for the final service, the wind suddenly began to blow fiercely and steadily. To the right of the speaker's platform was a door leading outside. Evidently the draughtproofing was loose, because the wind began to whip around and under the door, creating a deafening howl that drowned out every other sound in the small chapel.

To make matters worse, the chapel was not equipped with a sound system. And to make matters still worse, I have a voice that has never boomed in its life. If I had had a loud-speaker I still could not have been heard above the roar of the mountain wind.

As I sat there waiting to speak and making half-hearted efforts to be 'thankful in everything,' I remembered that the Lord had once been forced to deal with an unruly wind. He commanded it to be silent, I recalled. His promise in John 14:12 came to mind: 'Truly, truly, I say to you, he who believes in Me, the works that I do shall he do also; and greater works than these shall he do; because I go to the Father.' That promise began with *two* trulys, so I

figured it must really be true. Suddenly I found
myself praying, 'Lord, you surely didn't bring me
here to be upstaged by the wind. This is Your meeting; these are Your people. I am Your servant; and
that is Your wind. So I'm asking You in the name of
Jesus to muzzle the wind as Jesus did on the Sea of
Galilee.'

And then I did something I have never done
before or since. Almost without thinking what I was
doing, I began to speak to the wind (softly, you
understand; it seemed best that no one overhear me
carrying on a conversation with the wind), and I
commanded it to be still in the name of Jesus.

It was time for me to speak. The man who was to
introduce me was shaking his head in frustration and
pleading with the audience (who couldn't hear what
he was saying), to listen to me. As I moved to the
platform the wind suddenly stopped. It was as
though someone had thrown a switch. Quiet—
blessed, beautiful quiet settled over the chapel. And
during the entire time I spoke, not a howl, not even a
whimper, came from the wind. The 300 men heard
easily. I finished and sat down. Immediately the
switch was thrown and the wind took up where it had
left off. But the mountain had been cast into the sea
and the will of God done.

A Surprising Requirement: 'To Him Who Believes'

This kind of power, power to move mountains, is released only by faith. The father of the demon-possessed boy cried out to Jesus, 'If You can do anything...' to which Jesus replied, ' "If You can!" All things are possible to him who believes' (Mark 9:22, 23). The question is not, 'Can God do it?' but, 'Can I believe?' It is never a question of His ability but of our faith.

Let's take a closer look at the incident involving the boy and his father. Jesus, you remember, was on the Mount of Transfiguration with three of His disciples. The other nine waited in the valley below. While they waited, a father appeared with his son and asked them to deliver the boy from his tormented condition. It was not a far-fetched or surprising request, for since Jesus had bestowed upon them the power to cast out demons they had seen many such spirits flee at the mention of that name. But now something was wrong. In spite of all their efforts, they were powerless to free the boy.

When Jesus returned, the father reported the disciples' failure; and Jesus, taking charge of the situation, commanded the demon to leave the boy. Afterwards the puzzled disciples came to Jesus privately (I don't blame them for coming privately)— they must have been terribly embarrassed by their public failure) and asked why they had been unable to deliver the boy. Why were they suddenly unable to do what Jesus plainly promised them they could do (Matthew 10:1)?

It was a good question, for them and for us. Does it ever bother you – this terrible discrepancy between what God says we are and what we really are? God has promised us power; yet we are weak. He has promised to supply all our needs; yet we are forced to beg at the world's back door for money to keep our religious machines running. He promised that sin would not have dominion over us; and yet we are being delivered again into bondage. He promised that we would reign in life through Christ; yet we live like slaves, imprisoned by the world, the flesh, and the devil. Isn't it time we got alone with Jesus and asked why?

What is the answer? What reason did Jesus give? I was more than mildly shocked by the explanation put forth by a well-known theologian. Commenting on this incident in one of his books, he claimed that the gift to cast out demons bestowed upon the disciples by Jesus was a temporary one. The only thing wrong with that explanation is it is wrong. That was not the reason given by Jesus. He didn't say, 'You know, men, I knew there was something I forgot to tell you. That was a temporary gift and it expired yesterday at noon.'

Nor did He explain their failure by saying, 'Well, fellows, demons are tougher than they used to be. Why, I remember the time when just a snap of the fingers would send them running for cover. But times have changed.'

Forgive me if I sound irreverent. I don't intend to be; but some of the reasons we offer for our tragic impotence are just as irreverent—and just as wrong.

What *did* Jesus say? 'Because of the littleness of your faith; for truly I say to you, if you have faith as a mustard seed, you shall say to this mountain, "Move from here to there," and it shall move; and nothing shall be impossible to you' (Matthew 17:20). In Mark's account Jesus answered, 'This kind cannot come out by anything but prayer' (Mark 9:29). There is no real contradiction in the two answers, for prayer and faith are two sides of the same coin. Faith encourages us to pray and prayer is the true expression of our faith. (See Mark 11:23, 24.)

Jesus' answer is unmistakably clear—the secret of the disciples' failure was their lack of faith. No other reason is given, for no other reason exists. This calls to mind Matthew's comment concerning Jesus' ministry in His hometown of Nazareth: 'And He did not do many miracles there because of their unbelief' (Matthew 13:58).

Why Faith?

Why this divine insistence upon faith? The answer, I believe, revolves around three words: *grace, glory,* and *guarantee.*

Grace. In Romans 4:16, Paul says, 'For this reason it is by faith, that it might be in accordance with grace.' Grace can operate only through faith; that is the only environment in which it can exist. To set aside faith is to make grace inaccessible. Since grace is God's unmerited favour toward man, the only way man can receive it is by faith. If it comes to him because of his goodness or his parentage or anything else, it ceases to be unmerited; thus it ceases to be grace. And that is why man has such a hard time with faith: it strikes a fatal blow to his pride. It is extremely difficult and downright traumatic for human nature to sing a song like, 'Jesus paid it all; all to Him I owe.' Old Adam would choke on such words.

We have this need to contribute something; our ego demands it and feeds upon it. But faith forces us to admit that the things we truly need are beyond our power to produce and that only God can provide them. Calvin said, 'Faith brings a man empty to God, that he may be filled with the blessings of Christ.' Faith puts man right where God wants him— in the place of total dependence.

Glory. Faith glorifies God and brings honour to His name. Faith is man's positive response to the revealed character of God. Unbelief, therefore, is an assault upon God's character and an insult to His integrity. To disbelieve God is to deny that He is what He says He is; it calls into question His wisdom and power and goodness. That is why Spurgeon said that 'to trust in the Lord Jesus is the climax of virtue.'

Guarantee. Again in Romans 4:16, Paul gives

another clue as to why God demands faith: '...in order that the promise may be certain to all the descendants.' That the promise may be certain to all; and such certainty is possible only on the basis of faith. If any basis other than faith is required, then some will be excluded. For regardless of how easy and simple you make the requirement, some will be unable to meet it. But anyone, everyone, can believe.

Walter K. Price quotes one of his college professors as saying, 'The genius of Christianity lies in its method of accessibility, for it is both universal and democratic. Anyone can believe–from the president of the university to the garbage man!'[1] Christmas Evans used to say, 'I can take a man, tie him hand and foot, nail him in a barrel and shout through a knothole what he must do to be saved and he can do it!'[2]

What Is Your Mountain?

Have you found yourself saying, 'If it wasn't for this circumstance, I could be what God wants me to be?' Is there a specific something that is preventing you from fulfilling the will of God in your life? That is your mountain. And you can be certain you have one, for the Christian life is never unopposed. The Ship of Zion is a Man O' War, not a luxury liner. God expects us to face opposition from the world, the flesh, and the devil. But that unholy trinity and the mountains they pile up before us can be swept away by the weakest Christian who knows how to believe God.

Notes

1. Walter K. Price, *Revival in Romans* (Grand Rapids: Zondervan Publishing House, 1962), p. 25.
2. *Ibid.*, p. 25.

CHAPTER FIVE

The Wizard of Is

The Christian lives in two worlds. He is resident of this present evil age and of the Age to Come. Though he is a citizen of this world, the Bible says his 'citizenship is in heaven' (Philippians 3:20) and that already he is 'seated... with Him in heavenly places, in Christ Jesus' (Ephesians 2:6). As a believer he has been delivered 'out of this present evil age' (Galatians 1:4) and has 'tasted... the powers of the age to come' (Hebrews 6:5). Eternal life is a present possession. The Christian lives simultaneously in the physical world and in the spiritual world, in the seen and in the unseen, in the present and in the future, on earth and in heaven.

This new age, the Age to Come, dawned with the coming of Jesus into the world. His message was, 'The Age to Come *has* come!' and He demonstrated it by His power over death, disease, and the devil.

These two ages, the present evil age and the Age to Come, do not run in temporal succession but exist side by side. In other words, the Age to Come doesn't begin when this present evil age ends; it has already begun. It began 2000 years ago at Bethlehem. Somewhere in the future this present evil age will cease and only the new age continue; but for the present they are running on parallel tracks. While the kingdom of God will have a future visible manifestation, it has already arrived in the hearts of believers. We have already been delivered from 'the domain of darkness, and transferred...to the kingdom of His beloved Son' (Colossians 1:13). As a pledge of this we have been given the Holy Spirit (Ephesians 1:14).

The Christian can live a heavenly life on earth! He has tasted the powers of the Age to Come (Hebrews 6:5). Now a 'taste' isn't a seven-course meal, but it is just as real. The difference is in quantity, not in quality. And the quality of life that he will someday experience in heaven can be experienced right now on earth. Jesus taught us to pray for the will of God to be done on earth as it is presently being done in heaven (Matthew 6:10). 'A prayer such as this, taught us by the Lord Jesus, certainly must be one that can be fulfilled. We *can* do the will of God on earth as it is in heaven, or the prayer is mockery.'[1] This means that through the believer heaven can actually infiltrate earth.

If all this is true, and it is, why then do so many of us fail to experience this quality of life? There seems to be a great gulf fixed between what the Bible says we are and what we really are in daily experience. According to Paul, 'God has blessed us with every spiritual blessing in the heavenly places in Christ' (Ephesians 1:3). And Peter informs us that 'His divine power has granted to us everything pertaining to life and godliness' (2 Peter 1:3). We were meant to 'live...like kings' in this life (Romans 5:17, Phillips), but the average Christian is a spiritual pauper. How can this be?

Absolute And Appropriated

We must recognize the difference between the believer's *position in Christ* and his experience of that position. Writing of the sanctification of the believer, Merrill F. Unger says:

> It is at this point that confusion is interjected in the minds of so many believers. They fail to see that this is a *positional* truth—truth that applies to the mind and reckoning of God and concerns the eternal and unchangeable placement of the believer in Christ as the result of Christ's redemptive work on the cross.
>
> This *positional* truth must be differentiated and yet related to *experiential* truth. The latter has to do with the believer's comprehending and appropriating positional truth by faith, thereby making it realizable in his actual experience.... *Faith* in our position of sainthood in Christ conveys the benefits of sainthood into our experience.[2]

Everything God has done for the Christian is *absolute* but must be *appropriated*. For example, the sacrificial death of Christ was *absolute* in that He died for every man. God's love in Christ was directed at the whole world (John 3:16); and John the Baptist declared Jesus to be the 'Lamb of God who takes away the sin of the world' (John 1:29). In 1 John 2:2 we are told that Christ is 'the propitiation [*satisfaction, covering*] for our sins; and not for ours only, but also for those of the whole world.' But this does not mean that all are saved automatically. That absolute atonement must be appropriated by faith. The Bible says, 'He who believes in Him is not judged; he who does not believe has been judged already, because he has not believed in the name of the only begotten Son of God' (John 3:18).

The Bible also states that the devil was defeated absolutely and completely by the death of Christ. In Hebrews 2:14 we read that Christ died 'that through death He might render powerless him who had the power of death, that is, the devil.' And John tells us that 'the Son of God appeared for this purpose, that He might destroy the works of the devil' (1 John 3:8). The devil and all his cohorts were stripped of their power and disarmed by the cross of Christ (Colossians 2:15). Well, then, somebody ought to inform the devil of his defeat! He certainly doesn't behave like a conquered enemy. On the contrary, he goes about like a roaring lion, seeking someone to devour (1 Peter 5:8).

While the devil's defeat is *absolute*, it must be *appropriated*. It is our business to inform him in the name of Jesus that he is a defeated enemy; and we are told to 'resist him, firm in your faith' (1 Peter 5:9). Because Satan has been conquered, James can say with confidence, 'Resist the devil and he will flee from you' (James 4:7).

Another example of appropriating the absolute is found in Romans 6. In the first ten verses Paul establishes the fact that we have died with Christ. It is our identification with Christ in His death that frees us from a life of sin. That is our *position*. To make that position experiential, Paul tells us in verse 11: 'Even so consider yourselves to be dead to sin, but alive to God in Christ Jesus.' On this point Unger writes:

> Saints can and do sin when they fail to know and depend on their position of sainthood. Many saints do not know their placement as saints (Romans 6:1-10). Many who do know it do not believe it and thus constantly fail to convert its benefits into daily living (Romans 6:11).[3]

The believer must recognize his position in Christ with all its attending privileges and by faith appropriate it in daily experience. Our experience will be in direct proportion to our appropriation.

Speaking of our position, let's go back to Philippians 3:20 where Paul says, 'for our citizenship is in heaven.' The word *citizenship* signifies a colony of foreigners who, though living in a foreign country, live by the laws of their own country and model their lives after their native home. Philippi was a Roman colony whose inhabitants, though not actually in Rome, lived as though they were. They dressed like

Romans, talked like Romans, and even thought like Romans. Living in Philippi, they obeyed the laws of Rome. The meaning of Paul's statement is that since we are citizens of heaven we are to live according to the laws of heaven rather than the laws of earth.

We are doomed to failure if we try to live the heavenly (Christian) life according to the laws of this world. When Jesus rebuked Peter for his foolish remarks about avoiding the cross, He said, 'This view of yours is not from God but from men' (Matthew 16:23, Williams). The apostle Philip tried to operate by the laws of earth when Jesus asked him what could be done about feeding the five thousand. Just as most of us would have done, Philip dug into his pocket, counted his money, and evaluated the situation on the basis of earthly laws: 'Two hundred denarii worth of bread is not sufficient for them, for every one to receive a little' (John 6:7). Even Andrew fell into the trap; he said, 'There is a lad here, who has five barley loaves, and two fish; but what are these for so many people?' (John 6:9).

Israel was sentenced to forty years in the wilderness because in their expectations they limited the power of God to the laws of earth. The spies reported that the land was filled with giants; and Israel, being mere grasshoppers, could not possibly defeat them. After all, anybody with any sense at all knows a grasshopper can't whip a giant. That is the law of common sense, drafted by the wisest of human minds.

Jesus made it clear that we are not to live by the

principles of this world when, after rebuking Peter for using his sword in the garden, He told Pilate, 'My Kingdom is not of this world. If My Kingdom were of this world, then My servants would be fighting, that I might not be delivered up to the Jews; but as it is, My Kingdom is not of this realm' (John 18:36).

Living In The Heavenlies

God has blessed us with every spiritual blessing in Christ Jesus in the heavenly places (Ephesians 1:3). Notice the location of the blessings: *in the heavenlies*–the spiritual realm. That's where Christ is seated (Ephesians 1:20); that's where the believer lives (2:6); that's where the blessings are (1:3); that's where the action is (6:12). If these were the blessings of God in the 'earthlies' they could be obtained by earthly means. But being located in the heavenlies, they can be acquired by heavenly means only. When the astronauts went to the moon and brought moon-rocks back to earth, they had to forsake the laws of earth and operate by the laws of the moon. And if we are to bring the blessings of God to earth we must likewise abandon earthly laws and live by the laws of heaven.

To put it another way, God has deposited the riches of heaven in our account, but unless we know how to write cheques on that account we will spend our days in spiritual poverty.

So the big question is, *how*? How do we move heaven into earth? How do we make what is ours positionally ours experientially? How do we operate by the laws of heaven instead of the laws of earth?

The answer is *faith*. It is faith that appropriates the absolute and bridges the experience gap between what God says we are and what we really are.

Faith's part in this is stated in Hebrews 11:1, a key verse in the study of faith: 'Now faith is the substance of things hoped for, the evidence of things not seen' (AV). This is more than a definition of faith; it is a statement of faith's power and activity. This is what faith does.

As we saw in chapter four the 'things hoped for' are the things promised but not yet received. The 'things hoped for' embrace all the blessings and benefits of a citizen of heaven. The word *substance*, translated in the New American Standard Bible, *assurance*, is a very interesting Greek word. It can also be translated *confidence* or *guarantee*. Moulton and Milligan offer this definition:

> Used in Greek for property, estate, land-agreement of sale. It stands for the whole body of documents bearing on the ownership of a person's property, deposited in the archives and forming *the evidence of ownership*.... And as this is the essential meaning in Hebrews 11:1, we venture to suggest the translation 'Faith is the *title-deed* of things hoped for.'[4]

All the things God has promised belong to me as a member of His Kingdom family. They are mine;

they are my inheritance; I own them. But before I can take possession of them in experience, I must prove ownership; I must produce the title. This refers to faith, the 'title-deed of things hoped for.' Faith enables me to possess my possessions.

And now let's look at the most strategic word in that verse. When a writer of the Greek language wanted to give special emphasis to a certain word, he did so by placing that word first in the sentence. Our English translations rarely reveal this emphasis because it would make for awkward reading, and so we often miss the emphasis the writer intended. Now, can you guess which word is placed emphatically at the beginning of this verse? The little word *is*. I've had a great time with this Wizard of *Is*.

The writer wanted to emphasize the fact that faith makes things a present reality. Faith *is* substance. It is the title-deed to all God has promised. Notice that the verse doesn't say, 'Faith *brings* substance'; but rather, 'faith *is* substance.' Faith *is*, right now, at this very moment, the substance of things hoped for.

We often find ourselves praying something like this: 'Lord, I have faith. Now when are you going to reward my faith and give me the substance?' But faith does not say, 'I'm going to get it.' Faith declares, 'I have it.' By faith, things future, the things we hope for, become a present reality. Faith reaches into the future, lays its hand on the hoped-for things, and gives them to us. Faith isn't hoping; faith is having. As J. Oswald Sanders says, 'The function of faith is to turn God's promises into facts.'[5]

Three Kinds Of Faith

We can divide faith into three categories. First, there is the kind of faith that says, 'God can.' We believe God can do anything. Nothing is too hard for Him, for with God all things are possible. But this is not the victorious faith of which the Bible speaks. It is passive and accomplishes nothing. Suppose you have a great problem; and upon hearing that God is able and anxious to deliver you, you say, 'I believe God can solve my problem.' Is it solved? No. We may believe God can solve the problem; but simply believing God *can* do it doesn't meet the need.

Then there is the faith that says, 'God will.' This is better, but still short of the biblical ideal. You believe not only that God can solve your problem but that He will—someday. In the meantime you bite your nails, wring your hands, fret and fuss, and drive everyone within fifty miles crazy. There is more to real faith than believing God *will*.

The faith described in Hebrews 11:1 believes beyond God can and God will. It believes *God has*. This kind of faith declares it already done. Instead of waiting for God to create the provision, it steps into the provision already available. Isn't this what Jesus means in Mark 11:24? He says, 'Therefore I say unto you, What things soever you desire, when ye pray, believe that ye receive them' (AV). The word *receive* is a Greek aorist tense which implies you receive it before you actually have it. Williams translates it like this: 'So I tell you, whenever you pray and ask for anything, have faith that it has been granted to you, and you will get it.' Jesus literally is saying, 'Believe you have already got it and you'll get it.' That is just another way of saying, 'Faith is substance.' R. A. Torrey said that he worried for years over the grammar of that verse, until one day he stopped worrying about the grammar and started enjoying the promise.

Anyone can believe he has something *after* he receives it. That's walking by sight, not by faith. Biblical faith is believing you have something before you have it. You believe you have it because God says you have it and not because you see it in your hand.

Which Came First?

Most people believe God creates provision to meet our problem. When we run into a tough situation we plead with God to come through with a solution. But God doesn't create provisions to meet our problems. He creates problems (or, if you prefer, he *allows* problems) to meet His provisions.

Remember the man born blind, mentioned in John 9? The disciples asked Christ if the blind man or his parents were responsible for the problem. It was a perfectly natural question. But Jesus said, 'It was neither that this man sinned, nor his parents; but it was in order that the works of God might be displayed in him' (John 9:3).

We find the same principle in the creation account. God made provision for every creature before He made the creatures. He made water, then fish; animals, then vegetation. Adam didn't have to hold his breath until God could create some air to breathe. But that's how we usually react to prob- lems. We take a deep breath and hope God will hurry with a solution before we suffocate.

But God provides the supply before there is a need. Which came first, the last Adam or the first Adam? The last Adam. Which came first, sin or salvation? Paul tells us we were chosen in Christ before the foundation of the world (Ephesians 1:4). Revelation 13:8 speaks of Christ as the Lamb slain from the foundation of the world. Before there was a garden in Eden there was a cross on Calvary.

What does all this mean? It means that there exists no need in your life that God, by His grace, has not already met. He has already blessed us with every spiritual blessing and has already given us all things that pertain to life and godliness. But those provisions lie behind locked doors and only the key of faith can open them.

A good illustration of this is found in the experi- ence of Joshua as he led the people into Canaan. God said to him, 'Every place that the sole of your foot shall tread upon, that have I given unto you, as I said unto Moses' (Joshua 1:3, AV).

Further on, in Joshua 2:24, we read, 'And they said unto Joshua, Truly the Lord hath delivered into our hands all the land.' With the city of Jericho it was the same. 'And the Lord said unto Joshua, See, I have given into thine hand Jericho' (6:2). Every step

Joshua took was on conquered ground. And today's believer, whether he knows it or not, walks on conquered ground.

This kind of faith was the key that unlocked the land of Canaan. Forty years earlier, Israel had marched to the doors of the Promised Land but had failed to enter because they would not believe God had already given it to them. They feared defeat in battle. But Joshua brought them in because he knew theirs was not a *victory to be achieved* but a *victory to be received*. The land was theirs already. Grace made it available and faith accepted it.

Another Wizard of Is appears in 1 John 5:4: 'And this is the victory that has overcome the world–our faith.' For years I read that as though faith obtained the victory. I thought that if I believed long and hard enough, eventually the victory would be mine. But faith itself *is* the victory. The possession of faith constitutes victory.

Someone says, 'Do you mean to tell me that if I simply believe I have the victory, I *have* the victory?'

'That's right.'

'I don't believe it.'

'You don't have the victory either, do you?'

The phrase 'win the victory' betrays an inadequate understanding of the Cross work of our Lord. By His death Jesus won every victory for us. The tense of the verb *overcome* indicates that it has already been done and remains done. Just think of it–every temptation you will face today was overcome by Jesus 2,000 years ago! You have only to step into the victory already secured. That's living in the luxury of Calvary. And we enter that victory the same way we entered salvation—by grace through faith. Grace obtains the victory; faith maintains the victory.

This positional victory becomes experiential when the Christian stands before his besetting, binding habit, a weakness that hounds him day after day, and declares, 'Lord Jesus, I thank You that on the cross You delivered me from this. It has already been conquered by Your blood, and by faith I now accept Your victory over it and thank You that it is done.'

Let's examine one more Wizard of Is: 'My grace is sufficient for you' (2 Corinthians 12:9). I discovered this 'is' while going through a titanic trial sometime back. I knew God's grace could be, would be, sufficient. But in the meantime I was under the circumstance rather than on top of it. I kept wondering when God's grace was going to be sufficient. What was taking God so long to fulfil His promise? And one day as I walked down the street, wallowing in self-pity, this verse leaped into my mind shouting, '*IS!* My grace *is* sufficient. Not will be, but *is*.' For the first time I really saw the little word *is*. God's grace *is* sufficient; not can be or will be, but *is* right now, this very instant, sufficient. Standing in the middle of the street, I prayed, 'Lord, I see it! I thank You that right now Your grace is making me sufficient for this trial.' At that moment the verse came alive in my heart, the Holy Spirit made real what I had reckoned, and the grace of God became miraculously sufficient. When by faith I agreed with the

Word of God, the Spirit made experiential what had before been only positional.

From Pleading To Praising

Faith is substance. God first began teaching me this truth a few years ago when I had my back to the wall financially. I needed five hundred dollars immediately and I saw no way to get it. I had exhausted (or so I thought) every possibility. At the same time I got sick. It was the good kind of sickness–not well enough to go to work, but not too sick that I couldn't enjoy staying home. I said, 'This is of God. He has provided an opportunity for me to lock myself away and pray down the money.' And that's what I did– almost. I knelt beside my bed and opened my Bible to Matthew 6:33: 'But seek first His Kingdom and His righteousness; and all these things shall be added to you.' The 'all things' referred to the physical necessities of life Jesus talked about in the preceding verses. I knew God owned all the cattle on a thousand hills, that the silver and gold were His, and that it was up to me to pry (or pray–to me, they were the same) five hundred dollars out of His hands.

I prayed, 'Lord, meet my need. Lord, meet my need. Lord, are You going to meet my need? Give me a sign.' After praying like that for awhile I would read the verse over and over, trying to coax my bashful faith to the surface. Then I would renew my pleading and praying.

After about an hour of this the Lord seemed suddenly to say to me, 'Read the verse again.' I did. It hadn't changed. Then the Lord said something that shook me. 'Don't you wish your banker had said that instead of Me?'

I thought about that, knowing He was correct. What if my banker had promised me that if I would concentrate on seeking God and doing His will, he would provide all my necessities? I knew I wouldn't be worrying about a mere five hundred dollars. Nor would I be begging and pleading with him to keep his promise. He was an honest man. I would simply inform him of my need and rest assured it would be supplied.

The Lord seemed to say, 'Son, your problem is you have more faith in the word of a man than in the Word of God.' All my 'praying' had been unbelief in disguise. God, who is greater than man, cannot lie. And His resources far outweigh those of any bank. This God had promised that if I would simply seek first His kingdom and righteousness, all the material needs of my life would be met. Immediately I stopped pleading with God to meet my need and started praising Him for doing it. Within two days God provided the five hundred dollars. When I believed I already had it, I got it. Faith was substance.

There are heights of sweet communion that are
     awaiting me,
There are ocean depths of mercy that are flowing full and free;

There are precious pearls of promise that can
   ne'er be priced in gold,
There's a fulness in my Saviour that has never
   yet been told.

J. Stuart Holden

Notes

1. Wilber M. Smith, *The Biblical Doctrine of Heaven* (Chicago: Moody Press, 1968), p. 144.
2. Merrill F. Unger, *What Demons Can Do to Saints* (Chicago: Moody Press, 1977), p. 31.
3. *Ibid.*
4. James Moulton and George Milligan, *The Vocabulary of the Greek Testament* (Grand Rapids: Eerdmans Publishing Company, 1930), p. 660.
5. J. Oswald Sanders, *Prayer Power Unlimited* (Chicago: Moody Press, 1977), p. 43.

CHAPTER SIX

Believing Is Seeing

A new phrase has surfaced recently in the scientific community. It is 'parallel reality'. This is the name given to the theory that our universe may not be the only one around; another may exist parallel to it. We are unaware of its existence (if it does exist) because we lack the perceptive equipment to see it. Physical reality comes to us through the physical senses; remove one of those senses and immediately part of the physical world becomes, so to speak, a parallel reality.

To a blind man, for instance, a rainbow could be called a parallel reality. It exists, but he lacks the capacity to perceive it and would not even know of its existence unless someone else had told him about it. But give him the sense of sight, and the rainbow moves into his world and becomes a part of his physical reality.

Take a man who has never seen or heard of television. He is unaware that the air around him is filled with television programmes; they constitute a parallel reality. But plop him down in front of a TV set, turn it on, and suddenly the invisible becomes visible—the parallel reality becomes a physical reality. Interesting theory, isn't it? Some scientists even think this may explain UFOs!

Whether such a parallel reality exists, no one knows. It is just a theory. But I know of another parallel reality that does exist. There *is* an invisible world coexisting with our physical world. It is described in Colossians 1:16: 'In Him [Christ] all things were created, both in the heavens and on earth, *visible and invisible*, whether thrones or dominions or rulers or authorities–all things have been created through Him and for Him' (emphasis added).

There exists an invisible world that is more real than our visible world. As a matter of fact, this invisible world is the *ultimate reality*. Hebrews 11:3 tells us that 'the visible was made out of the invisible' (Moffatt). The explanation behind our universe is not physical but *spiritual*. This means that the ultimate reality is spiritual rather than physical, as is commonly supposed. What you *cannot* see is more real than what you can see!

This fact is brought out by Paul in 2 Corinthians. He says, 'While we look not at the things which are seen, but at the things which are not seen; *for the things which are seen are temporal; but the things which are not seen are eternal*' (4:18, emphasis added). Paul has been describing the physical sufferings involved in his service for Christ, sufferings that would wilt and wither the strongest of men. But, says the apostle, 'We do not lose heart.' He is afflicted, but not crushed; hard-pressed, but never hemmed in; always perplexed, but never to the point of despair; always persecuted, but never deserted;

knocked down, but not knocked out. And in the midst of these assaults he never loses heart, is never discouraged or driven to the point of throwing in the towel.

How does he withstand such pressure? He has discovered the secret of living in the unseen world, the world of eternity, the world of ultimate reality. And that secret is fixing his gaze upon and concentrating his attention upon (the literal meaning of the Greek word translated 'look') the things that are not seen instead of the things that are seen.

Paul saw the invisible. With the apostle John, Paul knew that this present world is passing away – but the will of God, and those who do it, abide forever (1 John 2:17).

This was Moses' secret also. Consider the unbelievable sacrifices he made in order to obey God. He 'refused to be called the son of Pharaoh's daughter; choosing rather to suffer ill-treatment with the people of God... considering the reproach of Christ greater riches than the treasures of Egypt' (Hebrews 11:24-26). The reproaches of Christ or riches – how could he make such an appraisal? Verse 27 provides the answer: 'He endured, as seeing Him who is unseen.' If ultimate reality to Moses had been the riches of Egypt he would have never left the palace. But rather than look upon the things that were seen (the pleasures and treasures of Egypt), he looked upon the things that were not seen (the riches of Christ – thousands of years before Christ was born!) and thus endured. Moses looked beyond the visible to the invisible and saw the ultimate reality—God.

Remember Elisha's faint-hearted servant? One morning as he prepared breakfast he glanced out the window and spotted the king's chariots surrounding the house. Terrified, he cried out to Elisha: 'Alas, my master! What shall we do?' The prophet calmly answered (I believe he may have stifled a yawn), 'Those who are with us are more than those who are with them.' Then he asked the Lord to raise the veil on the unseen world. 'And the Lord opened the servant's eyes, and he saw; and behold, the mountain was full of horses and chariots of fire all around Elisha' (2 Kings 6:15-17).

What *caused* the young man's defeatist attitude? He looked at the visible, thinking that what he saw with the eyes of flesh was the ultimate reality, the final word. What *cured* him? With the eyes of faith he looked beyond the visible to the invisible and realized that the ultimate reality is not what is seen but what is unseen. That was a case of parallel reality; the horses and chariots of fire were there all the time, but he lacked the perceptive apparatus to see them.

This ability to see and appreciate the things of the unseen spiritual world is one of the basic differences between the saved and the unsaved. The natural man, according to Paul, doesn't accept spiritual things, 'for they are foolishness to him, and he cannot understand them, because they are spiritually appraised' (1 Corinthians 2:14). But the Christian, because he has been equipped by the Spirit of God, knows 'the things freely given to us by God' (1 Corinthians 2:12).

What You Don't See Is What You Get

Without a doubt, one of the most vital secrets of successful Christian living is this ability to see the invisible. There exists, unseen by natural eye and unperceived by natural senses, a world of heavenly resources and divine power. The question is, how do we enter that invisible realm?

Hebrews 11:1 tells us. 'Faith...is the evidence of things not seen' (AV). Faith is the sixth sense that enables the believer to move into the unseen and eternal world. The word 'evidence' means *proof by demonstration*. In other words, faith doesn't merely convince us that unseen things exist; it brings them into the actual experience of our lives. It is evidence based on experience.

Faith is sight. Believing is seeing. If you want the key to the famous faith chapter, Hebrews 11, read through it, replacing the phrase 'by faith' with the words, *by seeing the invisible*. The heroes of faith were men and women who could see beyond the visible to the invisible and believed more in what they could not see than in what they could see. Our trouble is we believe that what we see is the final word on any subject.

Believing is seeing means we believe what God has said despite physical evidence to the contrary, and when there is no physical evidence to support what He has said.

An incident in John 20 illustrates this. The disciples are closeted in the upper room discussing in guarded tones the curious events following their Master's death. Suddenly the risen Christ appears, and the disciples see Him—all except the absent Thomas. Later when the excited disciples tell Thomas what happened, he scoffs and says, 'Unless I shall see in His hands the imprint of the nails, and put my finger into the place of the nails, and put my hand into His side, I will not believe' (John 20:25). *Unless I see I will not believe.*

Eight days later Jesus reappears. This time Thomas is present and Jesus invites him to touch the nailprints and to put his hand into his side. Shocked into belief, Thomas falls to his knees and cries, 'My Lord and my God!' Now observe how Jesus responded to Thomas' declaration of faith. 'Jesus said to him, "Because you have seen Me, have you believed? Blessed are they who did not see, and yet believed" ' (John 20:29).

In effect, Jesus classified those who believe into two categories: those who say, 'Seeing is believing'—'Unless I see I will not believe.' That's seeing with the eyes of flesh.

Then there are those who say, 'Believing is seeing'—'Blessed are they who did not see, and yet believed.' That's seeing with the eyes of faith. And upon those Jesus pronounced a blessing. Surely Peter was referring to this when, years later, he wrote: 'And though you have not seen Him, you love Him, and though you do not see Him now, but believe in Him, you greatly rejoice with joy inexpressible and full of glory' (1 Peter 1:8).

When Martha's faith faltered at the tomb of Lazarus, Jesus said, 'Did I not say to you, if you believe, you will see the glory of God?' (John 11:40). Ruled as we are by our physical senses, we try to reverse the order and say, 'First let me see the glory of God and then I'll believe.' The old hymn about the cross says, 'It was there by faith I received my sight.' But if we sang it honestly we would probably say, 'It was there by sight I received my faith.' Like the taunting Jews around the cross, we say, 'Let Him come down from the cross and then we will believe.'

If we are to live by faith we must not allow our physical senses—what we see, taste, touch, smell, and hear—have the last word. We must move out of the sense realm into the Scripture realm. If our five senses tell us one thing and the Scriptures quite another, we must believe the Scriptures.

A church member told me he couldn't afford to tithe. He had figured and figured, but there was no possible way he could do it. 'I've got it down in black and white,' he said. 'Figures don't lie.' Well, neither does the Bible. And if God tells us to do something, there is a way to do it. God never commands us to do anything without enabling us to do it—if we are willing. This man's problem was not that he figured— there's nothing unspiritual about that. But he figured wrong; he figured without faith. In adding his figures, he forgot to include the good promises of God. His conclusion was based solely on things visible.

Faith is the evidence of things not seen. You may not *see* deliverance from a nagging habit; you may not *see* the answer to your prayers; you may not *see* the inexhaustible supplies of God provided to meet your need. Then how do you know they are there? If you can't see, touch, taste, smell, or hear them, what proof do you have that they exist? Faith is the proof. We believe such things exist because God's Word says they do. Our faith rests not on physical evidence but on scriptural revelation. We choose to believe the promises of a God who cannot lie.

Saved From The Commotion Of Emotion

This understanding of faith frees us from the slavery of our feelings. The Bible, not our feelings, should determine our faith. Many Christians live by feeling instead of faith. Of course, there's nothing wrong with emotion; the capacity for emotional enjoyment is a gift from God. Let's face it—it feels good to feel good. But the abuse and misuse of emotion is a major problem of present-day Christianity and poses a real threat to spiritual maturity.

I've seen Christians kneel at an altar to commit themselves totally to Christ and claim the fullness of His Spirit, then rise from their knees with their finger on their pulse to see how they are doing. They want to hear angel wings flapping and feel goose bumps playing leapfrog up and down their spine. Then they will believe. But when we insist that God give additional confirmation beyond His Word, we void everything. We shouldn't ask God for additional proof about something He has stated plainly in His Word. Faith is its own fleece.

We tend to measure our spirituality by our emotional level. If we feel victorious then we must be victorious. We believe our prayers are getting through if we feel they are. Our feelings must say 'Amen' to our faith. But emotions are fickle and fleeting and not to be trusted. As a gauge of spirituality they are about as reliable as a sundial at midnight. Emotion is but the echo of an experience and destined to fade into nothingness.

This slavery to emotion can take us even further astray. If no satisfying and supportive feeling presents itself we may try to create, or recreate, a mood that corresponds to the spiritual exercise we are engaged in. C. S. Lewis was wise to this ploy of the devil, and in his *Screwtape Letters* exposed it through a letter Screwtape writes to his nephew, Wormwood. The old veteran demon is instructing the rookie in the best ways to draw Christians away from the Lord. He writes:

> Keep them watching their own minds and trying to produce feelings there by action of their own wills. When they meant to ask Him for charity, let them, instead, start trying to manufacture charitable feelings for themselves and

not notice that this is what they are doing. When they meant to pray for courage, let them really be trying to feel brave. When they say they are praying for forgiveness, let them be trying to feel forgiven. Teach them to estimate the value of each prayer by their success in producing the desired feeling; and never let them suspect how much success or failure of that kind depends on whether they are well or ill, fresh or tired, at the moment.

Trusting our feelings can be hazardous to our spiritual health. If our last prayer time was attended by ecstatic emotions, we may believe that unless the same feelings reappear the next time we pray, something is wrong with us. If we are engulfed with rapturous feelings while preaching, we are apt to think that that kind of feeling is heavenly evidence that we are preaching in the Spirit. And when next we stand to speak, if the remembered feeling is absent, we plunge into despair, thinking God has abandoned us or has withdrawn His Spirit. At that precise moment, Satan seizes us by the throat of our guilt complex and shouts, 'Aha! See, God has counted you unworthy. You may as well give up this work.'

The Welsh revival that took place in the early years of this century was one of the most extraordinary works of God that modern history has witnessed. Evan Roberts, the unofficial leader of the revival, was greatly used of God and thus became a prime target for the deceptive tactics of the enemy. A close friend has preserved a report of two intimate experiences that bear upon this point.

The first of these occurred while Roberts was praying prior to a service in which he was to preach. As he prayed, the whole room was suffused with a dazzling glow and there seemed to be a creature of light standing close by. Roberts assumed it was an angel of the Lord. It was an exhilarating experience, and in subsequent times of prayer, he found himself expecting the phenomenon to be repeated. It never was.

The second experience came as he was sitting on the platform awaiting his time to preach. Suddenly there was thrust into his mind the number 'fifty-seven'. He was perplexed at his preoccupation with this figure and wondered what it meant. That night fifty-seven people trusted Christ as Saviour. Again he was thrilled with the thought that he had been given a special revelation as to how many people would be converted. Subsequently he found himself waiting for similar information in other services. Like the experience with the brilliant light, it never happened again.

Later Evan Roberts came to the conviction that both these occurrences originated with the devil and were diversionary tactics designed to move him out of the spiritual realm into the sensual and sensational.

This does not mean that God will not allow us occasional emotional highs. But if we demand an emotional verification of His Word, He will probably withhold it, lest our faith rest on the feeling rather than the Word. Otherwise, when the feeling subsides, our faith will collapse.

I'm convinced that God wants to bring us to the place where we trust in Him and Him alone, without the aid of emotional crutches. Jesus desires in us the same quality of faith He sought in Jairus. You will remember, this father had a daughter at the point of death. At his request, Jesus agreed to go to the man's house and heal the girl. On the way they met a woman who had been haemorrhaging for twelve years and Jesus took time to help her. By the time Jesus was ready to resume his journey to Jairus' house, one of the father's servants arrived with the news that the girl was dead. When Jesus heard that He said to Jairus, 'Do not be afraid any longer; only believe, and she shall be made well' (Luke 8:50). Now Jesus had him right where He wanted him—and us.

As long as the girl was alive there was something visible, something tangible to cling to; there was something concrete to support his faith. But with the girl's death, the only thing he could cling to was the promise of Jesus. And that was enough. You can be sure that God will so work in our lives to bring us to the place where all we have to hang on to is the bare Word of God. And that is what faith is all about.

I do my hardest work before breakfast—getting up. Getting up is a lousy way to start the day. I never feel spiritual in the morning. And Sunday mornings are the worst. This is a real problem when you are a pastor with a congregation expecting you to deliver an inspiring and enthusiastic sermon. For years this troubled me to the point of despair. Saturday night I would go to bed feeling great–and spiritual. I would be excited about the coming Lord's Day and anxious to preach, convinced the Lord was going to bless in a mighty way. But during the night God would slip away and hide from me.

I know confession is good for the soul–but it can be bad for the reputation. Well, I have a confession to make. When I awoke on Sunday mornings, I felt so unspiritual, the last thing I wanted to do was preach. I spent most of the morning trying to figure out what I had done to cause God to abandon me. As silly as it seems now, this was very real then, and continued to cripple me until God taught me that my feelings have nothing whatsoever to do with my relationship to Him.

Our relationship is based on fact, not feeling. And the fact was, I was just as right with God when I awoke on Sunday morning as I had been when I went to sleep Saturday night. I may have lost the feeling, but that did not mean I had lost the victory.

If you are limping around on the crutches of feelings, throw them away and walk on the legs of faith.

Saved From The Treason Of Reason

So much for emotion, but what about reason? Is faith contrary to reason? Am I not to think at all? Do reason and logic have a place in the life of faith?

These are good questions, for we are often made to think that faith and reason are antagonists. I heard a preacher say once that if God was to reveal truth to us, we must stop thinking. 'If you thought it,' he said, 'God didn't reveal it.' Not so. It is through our renewed mind that God transforms us and reveals His will to us (Romans 12:2).

Faith is not contrary to reason; it simply goes beyond it. Faith refuses to be limited by the boundaries of logic, and this may sometimes leave the impression that it is illogical.

When the twelve spies returned from their investigation of Canaan, ten of them said the land was filled with giants and it was not reasonable to think that grasshoppers could whip giants. And they were correct. Their conclusion was perfectly logical. But two of the spies, Joshua and Caleb, held a different opinion and believed the land could be won. They didn't ignore the existence of the giants, but neither did they ignore the faithfulness of their God who had promised them victory in battle. Faith doesn't hide from the facts.

The ten spies went no further than their reason could carry them; Joshua and Caleb went as far as reason could take them, then allowed faith to carry them the rest of the way. Faith transcends reason and goes beyond it.

Suppose you want to go to America. You get in your car and drive to Lizard Peninsula and there you run into the Atlantic Ocean. As far as you know, there's no such thing as a trans-atlantic bridge, and

you know your car won't float. You have gone as far
as you can by that means of transportation. What do
you do now, give up and turn back? No. You are not
limited to one mode of travel. Instead of letting your
car limit your trip, you drive to an airport, board an
aeroplane and fly the rest of the way. The plane
doesn't deny or contradict your car; it rises above it;
it transcends it.

The car carries you to a certain point; then the
plane carries you beyond it. So it is with reason and
faith. God intends us to use our heads. After all, He
created, regenerated, and renewed our minds so we
could think and reason as Christians should. But He
doesn't mean for us to be limited by what seems
reasonable to finite minds. Human reason, even
regenerated human reason, has a limited range and
can carry us so far. Then faith must take over. Faith
continues and completes the trip reason begins.

While the ability to reason is God-given, it is
nonetheless restricted to physical evidence and
senses. And if we trust in reason alone, it will betray
us. Reason cannot breathe the rarified air of the
heavenlies.

Unlimited by reason and unaffected by feelings,
faith enables us to penetrate the barrier between the
visible and the invisible and reach into the heavenly
world to lay hold of 'things hoped for' and 'things not
seen.'

PART TWO
Faith
Exercised

CHAPTER SEVEN

Faith That Pleases God

What do you think of when you hear the word faith? I'll tell you what I think of. I think of *miracles*. The sound of the word calls forth visions of the dead being raised, mountains being cast into the sea, armies being put to flight, the laws of nature being suspended. All these have been attributed to the exercise of faith. But there is another miracle effected by faith, more miraculous than any of these—though it is seldom recognized and little appreciated. It is spoken of in Hebrews 11:5, 6:

> By faith Enoch was taken up so that he should not see death; and he was not found because God took him up; for he obtained the witness that before his being taken up he was pleasing to God.
>
> And without faith it is impossible to please Him, for he who comes to God must believe that He is, and that He is a rewarder of those who seek Him.

The noteworthy miracle in this story is not the detour Enoch took around death to get to heaven, but the fact that he was *pleasing to God*.

Faith is given, not that we may perform miracles, but that we may please God—which is the greatest miracle of all. The devil can work miracles, but he cannot please God.

Nothing greater can be said of us than that which was said of Enoch: 'He was pleasing to God.' And if this cannot be said of us, whatever else may be said is meaningless. For in this statement we find the purpose for which we were created and the standard by which our life is judged.

But the thing that captivates me most about Hebrews 11:6 is not the fact that we should be pleasing to God, but that we *can* be. Just think of it: fallen, sinful, selfish, finite people are able to please a thrice holy God, a God too pure even to look upon sin.

This is even more amazing when we remember how difficult it is to please *man*. Difficult? It's impossible. Not even God can please man. But, while we cannot please man with his low and lowering standards of right and wrong, and his incomplete knowledge of the real us, we can please a holy God who knows us through and through and from whom nothing can be hidden.

And this is accomplished by faith. The tense of the verb *please* indicates that apart from faith there is not a single moment when we are pleasing to God. Regardless of what we do, no matter how wonderful and sacrificial the act—apart from faith, it is unacceptable to God.

'Without faith it is impossible to please Him.' But

what kind of faith? 'He who comes to God must believe.' Believe what? That's what I like about the Bible–it never gives a mandate without giving the means of fulfilling it. We are told exactly, and very simply, what we must believe if we are to please God. The writer points to two things: if we are to please God we must believe that *God is real* and that He is a *Rewarder*.

God Is Real

'He who comes to God must believe that He is.' At first glance it appears the writer is saying that he who comes to God must believe there is a God to come to; he must believe in the existence of God. But he surely means something more than this, because the people to whom he is writing are Christians; they already believe in the existence of God. To tell them they must believe there is a God would be unnecessary.

And what's more, to tell someone who wants to come to God that he must first believe there is a God to come to doesn't make sense. After all, he wouldn't be coming to God if He didn't believe there was a God, would he? That would be like asking someone how to get to New Orleans and being told, 'First, you've got to believe there is a New Orleans.'

No, I think he is referring to something more. Let me paraphrase the statement, adding a few words, and I think we will get at what the writer had in mind:

'He must believe that God *still* is, *even when it looks like He isn't.*'

The people the author is addressing were undergoing furious persecution. Persecution wasn't new to them; they had 'endured a great conflict of sufferings' following their conversion to Christ some years before (Hebrews 10:32). But this time it was so fierce some were about to throw in the towel. The author was urging them to remain steadfast and faithful.

'We are not,' he says, 'of those who shrink back to destruction, but of those who have faith to the preserving of the soul' (Hebrews 10:39). And that's why Hebrews 11 was written—to remind these fellow believers that God had in times past proven Himself faithful in delivering His people, even when the prospects for deliverance were bleak. Remember, the writer cries, we are of those who have faith to the preserving of the soul. And that is the kind of faith that declares, 'God is,' even when it looks as though He isn't.

This is an affirmation of faith made in the face of overwhelming odds and contradictory circumstances.

At times it looks as if God isn't. Oswald Chambers speaks of those occasions when God withdraws 'His conscious blessings' in order to teach us to walk by faith.[1] I doubt that God ever totally withdraws His blessings, but He may withdraw for a season those conscious or obvious blessings.

One of my favourite Old Testament characters is Gideon. In Judges 6 we find Israel suffering under the Midianite yoke of bondage. Gideon is beating out wheat at the winepress and hiding it from the Midianites, when suddenly an angel takes a seat under a nearby oak tree and says to Gideon, 'The Lord is with you, O valiant warrior' (Judges 6:12).

Gideon probably jumped six feet off the ground when the angel spoke without warning. The angel may have been stretching it a bit by calling Gideon a 'valiant warrior'. Do you remember what Gideon said in response to the angel's greeting? 'Oh my Lord, if the Lord is with us, why then has all this happened to us? And where are all His miracles which our fathers told us about...? But now the Lord has abandoned us and given us into the hand of Midian' (Judges 6:13).

If the Lord is with us, why then has all this happened to us? Gideon's theology was simple, not to say appealing: If God is with us, then nothing bad can happen and we will experience a miracle a day as proof of His presence.

Unfortunately, Gideon's miracle-a-day theology is still with us, stronger than ever. It is preached, mostly on TV by the Joy-boys, that if we are filled with the Spirit and trust the Lord we will always be healthy and wealthy, that we will have 'all honey, no bees; no work, all ease.'

On Thanksgiving Day, 1975, our eighteen-year-old son took his life. Earlier that year he had been diagnosed as having a mood disorder caused by a chemical imbalance in the blood. We knew there was danger of suicide, but we had taken all the medical precautions possible and had covered him with believing prayer. We had no doubt God would deliver him from this elusive and deceptive malady. When he died, it looked as though God had abandoned us and we felt like crying with Gideon, 'If the Lord is with us, why then had all this happened?' But in spite of our traitorous thoughts and unwelcome feelings, we knew God was with us—that *God is*, even though at the time it looked like He wasn't.

Not long after Ron, Jr.'s, death I received a letter from some Christian friends in another state. They had heard of the tragedy and wanted to express their sympathy. But more than that, his death had unsettled their Gideon-shaped theology. They had a son about Ron's age and they said, 'We know that you are a man of God and that you have dedicated your life to serve the Lord. We don't understand how *something like this could happen to you*.' They figured that somehow my commitment to Christ deserved special treatment from the Lord and earned me a certain immunity from disaster.

But the fact is, loving God doesn't guarantee a charmed life. No exception from dark days is promised those who trust in Christ. We remain a part of the human situation, and there are times when it looks like God *isn't*.

Habakkuk wrestled with a similar problem. In his day it was the Chaldeans who kept rewriting his theology. They had laid siege to the city and were threatening to annihilate the people. Judah was finished—unless God intervened. Habakkuk the prophet had been storming the citadel of heaven with passionate prayers, but so far God had done nothing. Finally, in despair, the prophet cried, 'How long, O Lord, will I call for help, and Thou wilt not hear?' (Habakkuk 1:2). Why don't you do something, Lord? The Chaldeans are about to destroy us. That was his complaint. And then in the fifth verse, God answered, informing Habakkuk that He had done something but that the prophet wouldn't believe his ears. 'For behold, I am raising up the Chaldeans' (Habakkuk 1:6). The very thing that made him think God was doing nothing was the very thing God was doing!

Occasionally someone will say to me, 'God has really started working in my life.' But God is always at work in our lives. He has never 'started'. What we really mean when we say that is, 'God has finally started acting the way we expect Him to.' But sometimes the very things that cause us to believe God is not at work constitute the very work God is at.

'And Others'

I love Hebrews 11, especially the last part beginning with verse 32, where the writer really flies. 'And what more shall I say? For time will fail me if I tell of...'

And then, like a typical preacher, he tells of what he doesn't have time to tell of:

Who by faith conquered kingdoms, performed

acts of righteousness, obtained promises, shut the mouths of lions, quenched the power of fire, escaped the edge of the sword, from weakness were made strong, became mighty in war, put foreign enemies to flight... (vv. 33, 34).

That's great isn't it? That's the kind of faith I want.

'And others were tortured–' (v. 35).

Oops. Must have misread that last bit. I'll try it again.

'And others were tortured.'

That's what I was afraid of–I read it correctly the first time.

And others were tortured, not accepting their release...and *others* experienced mockings and scourgings, yes, also chains and imprisonment. They were stoned, they were sawn in two, they were tempted, they were put to death with the sword; they went about in sheepskins, in goatskins; being destitute, afflicted, illtreated... (Hebrews 11:35-37).

Is this the same faith spoken of in the earlier verses? I'm afraid so. The same faith that enabled some to escape death by the sword enabled others to endure death by the sword. Faith does not always wear the dazzling, silky purple of triumphant deliverance – often it is garbed in the blood-caked rags of triumphant death. But to say one is inferior to the other is to reveal an awful ignorance of the ways of God. The same faith that enables some to escape, enables others to endure.

Vance Havner is a friend. For over fifty years this mountain-bred prophet has ministered to thousands through his preaching and writing. His wife, Sara, was one of the 'and others'. Of the more than thirty books he has written, none has helped more people than his account of Sara's illness and subsequent death. Let me quote from *Though I Walk Through the Valley*.

I had hoped for the miraculous healing of Sara and that we might bear a dramatic testimony to the direct intervention of God. I had a sermon ready. But it was not to be.... It did not please God to heal her....

My disappointment was intense but sober thinking has changed my view. If a dramatic experience of healing had been ours it would have been sensational, but such experiences are rare and my listeners would have said, 'That is wonderful but it happens only once in a while and is the exception that proves the rule. Most of us do not have such miracles. Our loved ones die, our hopes fade, and we need a word for those who walk the Valley with no happy ending

to the story.' I can see now that God denied me
what I sought that I might bring a message to
the multitude like myself whose prayers were
not answered as hoped....

So I preach and write for a host of fellow
travellers through the Valley whose hopes, like
mine, were not realized and whose deepest
wish was not granted. If we can move through
this Valley and come out in victory, we have
found a greater blessing than if our personal
wish had been fulfilled in some miraculous
way.[2]

I have an idea that for most of us the problem is
not that we lack sufficient faith to be healed—we lack
sufficient faith to remain sick if that be God's will. It
requires greater faith to endure than to escape, I
imagine, and it is easier to believe that *God is* when
it looks as though He is than to believe *He is* when it
looks as though He isn't. And that is the kind of faith
that pleases God.

God Is A Rewarder

'He who comes to God must believe... that He is a
rewarder of those who seek Him' (Hebrews 11:6).

Let's break this down and examine each phrase
separately.

He is a rewarder. The faith that pleases God
believes that it is always worthwhile to seek the
Lord, regardless of how fruitless it may appear to be.

Those who set their hearts to honour Him by seeking Him with all their strength will not go unrewarded.

God is no man's debtor. This was brought home to the disciples in Mark 10. After sadly watching the rich young ruler walk away from eternal life, Jesus spoke of the difficulty of such rich people being saved. At that Peter said, 'Behold, we have left everything and followed You' (Mark 10:28). Perhaps Peter expected Jesus to be impressed with this and praise them for their great sacrifice. But such was not the case. To Peter's words of self-congratulation, Jesus said, 'Truly I say to you, there is no one who has left house or brother or sisters or mother or father or children or farms, for My sake and for the gospel's sake, but that he shall receive a hundred times as much...' (Mark 10:29, 30).

Not long ago I talked with a woman who prayed every day for five years that a certain broken relationship within her family would be healed. 'But in the end,' she said, 'it wasn't. God did not answer my prayers.'

I thought: every day for five years, and then, not answered. I said, 'Do you consider that those five years of praying were wasted?'

'Oh, no,' she said. 'I'm sorry if I gave that impression. In a way, those were the best five years of my life. I've never had a greater sense of God's presence and love.'

She hesitated a moment, then said, 'I hope you won't misunderstand what I'm about to say–but the five years of unanswered prayer and family problems

—well, what God has done for me in that time is well
worth it. If I could trade my unanswered prayers for
what the Lord did for me, I wouldn't.'

Those who seek. The Authorised Version reads,
'that diligently seek him,' which is better because the
word translated *seek* is a compound verb, *seek out*,
and 'the preposition in compound always seems to
denote that the seeker "finds", or at least exhausts
his power of seeking.'[3] God is the Rewarder of those
to whom His reward is worth the effort of exhausting
themselves seeking. It is the attitude of the shepherd
who goes out into the cold, damp night to search for
one lost sheep *until he finds it*. It is the attitude of the
woman who sweeps and searches her house for a lost
coin *until she finds it*. It is the attitude of Jacob,
wrestling with the angel, crying out, 'I will not let
you go until you bless me.' No halfhearted search
will uncover this treasure. God has a way of hiding
Himself from the casual looker.

The faith that pleases God is the kind that believes
His reward is worth whatever it takes to find it.

That seek Him. I think if *I* had written this verse I
would have worded it differently. Something like,
'He is a rewarder of those who seek the *reward*.'
Makes sense to me. After all, if what I need is the
reward, shouldn't it be the reward I am seeking? If I
need healing, shouldn't I seek healing? If financial
help, shouldn't I seek finances? But the reward goes
to those who seek not the reward, but the Rewarder.

Seek For Nothing More

I believe that the prayer-seeking of many believers goes unrewarded because they are seeking the wrong thing–the reward. They are seeking, not His face, but His hand. We are to seek Him and Him alone, because everything we need is in Him.

My favourite passage is Colossians 2:9, 10: 'For in Him all the fullness of Deity dwells in bodily form, and in Him you have been made complete.' What can be added to completeness? All the fullness of the Godhead dwells in Him; everything that is good and godly is in Him.

Think of it this way: He doesn't give peace, He *is* our Peace; He doesn't give knowledge, He is our knowledge; He doesn't give wisdom and righteousness and sanctification and redemption–He is all these things Himself (1 Corinthians 1:30).

Charles Wesley said it this way:

> Thy gifts alone cannot suffice,
> Except Thou be given,
> For Thy presence makes my paradise,
> And where Thou art is heaven.

Faith that pleases God loves Him for Himself and not for what it can get out of Him.

Several years ago, while I was conducting a conference in a Southern state in the USA, one of the church members asked me to come to his house and anoint him with oil, lay hands on him, and pray for his healing. As a Southern Baptist minister I don't get many requests like that. That night he told me of his problem. It had something to do with his hip joint, and although he had had several operations, he still could not walk without crutches. In the course of the conversation, he let me know that I was not the first preacher he had approached. As a matter of fact, he contacted every preacher who came through his city. And some of them were 'biggies' in the healing ministry. That struck me as strange. If God chooses to heal us, surely it doesn't take Him thirty-seven preachers to do it. Something was not right. So I asked him a simple question.

'Why do you want to be healed?'

He seemed surprised that I would ask such an obvious question. Then he said, 'It's like this. I belong to a prayer group—we meet every Monday night. And everyone in the group has a healing testimony except me. I'm the only member of the group who can't give a healing testimony.'

As he talked further it became obvious that the others in his prayer group were growing suspicious of his spirituality because of his inability to get healed. Here was a brother who was seeking the reward instead of the Rewarder.

When I first started travelling I made it a point to bring something home for the children—a souvenir or toy—nothing expensive, just something to surprise them. Soon the highlight of Dad's homecoming was the opening of the suitcases, because somewhere beneath the soiled shirts and dirty socks lay a surprise. The kids hardly noticed me—they were too anxious to get to the suitcase. It got so bad that my wife tried to coach them on how to behave when they saw me.

'Now, kids,' she would tell them, 'act like you're glad to see Daddy.'

But, bless their hearts, they were poor students of good manners when there were suitcases to be opened and treasures to be found. To tell the truth, at times it hurt just a bit—they seemed more interested in the cheap little trinkets I brought them than in the one who brought them—me, their loving father. But after all, they were just children.

The children are nearly grown now, and I still bring them gifts from distant and exotic places, like Tulsa, Oklahoma and Omaha, Nebraska. I've noticed something, though. They actually seem happier to see *me* than what I have brought them. But after all, they are no longer children.

> Once it was a blessing,
> Now it is the Lord.
> Once it was a feeling,
> Now it is His Word.
> Once His gifts I wanted,
> Now the Giver own.
> Once I sought for healing,
> Now Himself alone.
> *A.B. Simpson*

Faith that pleases God believes that God is better than His best gifts.

Settle For Nothing Less

After making the pivotal statement of verse 6, the writer calls upon some of the patriarchs of the past to reinforce his word with their testimonies. A phrase in Abraham's testimony intrigues me. It's found in verse 9. Speaking of Abraham and his journey to the Promised Land, the writer says, 'By faith he lived as an alien in the land of promise, as in a foreign land, dwelling in tents with Isaac and Jacob, fellow-heirs of the same promise.' The phrase I'm referring to is this one: 'He lived as an alien in the land of promise.' When at long last he finally reached the land of promise, the land God had given him for an everlasting possession, Abraham lived as an alien. He lived like a foreigner in his own country. And rather than build permanent dwellings, he lived in tents, the mark of a nomad, a transient. Why? Why didn't he build a solid house and live as a citizen in his own land of promise?

The Scripture says that Abraham, when he was called, obeyed and travelled under sealed orders to the place God gave him. We naturally assume that when God called Abraham, it was to the land that He had called him, and that's true. But I believe there is a truer sense in which God always calls us to Himself, that every call *from* God is a call *to* God. God Himself is our inheritance, and the promises He makes are the means He uses to draw us to Him.

At the risk of sounding irreverent, I believe the land was the carrot that God held in front of Abraham to get him to move out. What God had in mind

for Abraham beyond the land was a deeper knowledge of and closer fellowship with Himself. And
when Abraham finally arrived in the land of promise, he had come to know God in a far deeper and
richer way–and the land meant little to him.

He was now 'looking for a city which has foundations, whose architect and builder is God' (Hebrews
11:10). No wonder that he was able to unselfishly
offer his nephew Lot first choice of the land. Abraham had discovered something better than the land–
the Lord. Even in the land, his own land, Abraham
and the others confessed that they were strangers
and exiles on the earth. For 'they desire a better
country, that is a heavenly one' (Hebrews 11:16).

That is where faith finds its rest, its promised land;
not in the transient blessings of this age, but in the
very presence of God. The faith that pleases God
lives as an alien in the land of promise.

Throughout Hebrews 11 runs the hint that no visible, material, or earthly fulfilment could satisfy their
faith. Even in the land of promise they claimed to be
strangers and exiles *in the earth*–not just in Egypt,
but anywhere in the earth. And pilgrims and
strangers they remained. Faith will do nothing but
make you a stranger on this earth. If you are looking
for anything else, forget it. Faith doesn't necessarily
make life easier or more pleasant or more pros-
perous. The purpose of faith is to wean us from all
else beside, till alone with Jesus we are satisfied.

Dr R. E. O. White has a good word on this. He
writes:

It is indeed characteristic of spiritual life that God's people are strangers and pilgrims on the earth, sojourners and travelers who have not arrived.... It is the essential nature of pilgrim faith to continue seeking what it has not found, aiming for goals it has glimpsed but has not reached.

There is a maturer faith than the faith that asks and gets; it is the faith that asks and goes without, patiently without complaint.... Mature faith does not live by answers to prayer, but by prayer.

Faith demands more than earth can give, and so must always be disappointed on earth.... Faith is a perpetually defeated thing which never accepts defeat. Because it knows, when it pauses to reflect, that its disappointment is but the measure of its hopes; its goal is too big to be attained just yet.[4]

The faith that pleases God believes that He is a Rewarder of those who seek Him. And what is that reward? It is Himself. To Abraham He said, 'Fear not, Abram; I am thy shield, and thy exceeding great reward' (Genesis 15:1, AV). God is both the Rewarder and the Reward.

My heart has no desire to stay where doubts
    arise and fears dismay;
Tho' some may dwell where these abound, my
    prayer, my aim is higher ground.

I want to live above the world, tho' Satan's
    darts at me are hurled;
For faith has caught the joyful sound, the song
    of saints on higher ground.

I want to scale the utmost height and catch a
    gleam of glory bright;
But still I'll pray till heav'n I've found,
    'Lord, lead me on to higher ground.'

Notes

1. Oswald Chambers, *My Utmost for His Highest* (New York: Dodd, Mead & Co., 1935), p. 305.
2. Vance Havner, from *Though I Walk Through the Valley* (Old Tappan: Fleming H. Revell, 1974), pp. 80, 81. Copyright © 1974 by Fleming H. Revell Company.
3. Fritz Rienecker, taken from *A Linguistic Key to the Greek New Testament*, Vol. II (Grand Rapids: Zondervan Publishing House, 1980), p. 361. Copyright © 1980 by The Zondervan Corporation. Used by permission.
4. R. E. O. White, *The Exploration of Faith* (Chicago: Moody Press, 1969), pp. 112-115.

CHAPTER EIGHT

Believing God– A Case History

O nce upon a time a four-year-old, wanting to impress his parents, memorized part of the multiplication table. Standing at attention, he carefully recited, 'Two times two equals four.' Daddy beamed with pride. Mummy purred with delight. As they had suspected, their little darling was a genius. In the midst of their beaming and purring, the little boy asked, 'What's a two?'

I suspect many Christians approach faith in the same way. While declaring, 'I believe God,' under their breath they are asking, 'What's a believe?' The question rarely surfaces because everyone, of course, knows what it means to believe God, and no one wants to admit he does not know what everyone knows. And so they all stumble along the path of faith, suppressing the nagging fact that they don't really know how to exercise faith in God. For them there is a great gulf fixed between their claim to faith and their ability to believe God.

But to live the life of faith you must understand what is involved in believing God and 'how to go about it.'

In school the teacher could spend all day explaining how a certain math problem was solved, but until she actually worked out the problem on the black-board, I couldn't grasp it. And it is the same with faith. We need to observe someone actually believ-ing God. The Word must become flesh; the abstract must become concrete; and things invisible must be made visible. Truth is easier to grasp when clothed with flesh and blood, when theological propositions become historical persons. Faith requires this kind of incarnation. Of all the great biblical concepts, faith may well be the most abstract, the most intangible. It would help if we could watch someone go through the motions of believing God. We need to see some-one do it.

And that is the object of this chapter. We are going to become apprentices in the work of faith. Our teacher is Abraham. He is our word made flesh. Biblically, the name of Abraham is synonymous with faith; he is the father of the faith and of the faithful. No other figure demonstrates so ideally what it means to believe God. His life is a monument to the declaration, 'The just shall live by faith.'

Romans 4 presents a clear picture of Abraham's faith. Here Paul shows step by step how Abraham exercised his faith in God and that it was reckoned to him as righteousness (4:22). In other words, every-thing Abraham needed, everything God demanded of him, was obtained by his faith. And then Paul says, 'Now not for his sake only was it written, that " IT WAS RECKONED TO HIM," but for our sake also, to whom it will be reckoned' (4:23, 24). In preserving this account of Abraham's faith, God is not merely recording history, but presenting Abraham as the standard of faith for all believers. He is the representative man when it comes to faith. What was true of him is true of all those who believe as he believed. This fact is reinforced by the phrase in verse 16: '...those who are of the faith of Abraham, who is the father of us all.' If we believe as Abraham believed, we will receive as Abraham received.

The passage describing Abraham is a classical presentation of faith.

Verse 16: 'For this reason it is by faith, that it might be in accordance with grace, in order that the promise may be certain to all the descendants, not only to those who are of the Law, but also to those who are of the faith of Abraham, who is the father of us all.'

Verse 17: '(As it is written, "A FATHER OF MANY NATIONS HAVE I MADE YOU") in the sight of Him whom he believed, even God, who gives life to the dead and calls into being that which does not exist.'

Verse 18: 'In hope against hope he believed, in order that he might become a father of many nations, according to that which had been spoken, " SO SHALL YOUR DESCENDANTS BE." '

Verse 19: 'And without becoming weak in faith he contemplated his own body, now as good as dead, since he was about a hundred years old, and the deadness of Sarah's womb.'

Verse 20: 'Yet, with respect to the promise of God, he did not waver in unbelief, but grew strong in faith, giving glory to God.'

Verse 21: 'And being fully assured that what He had promised, He was able also to perform.'

Verse 22: 'Therefore also IT WAS RECKONED TO HIM AS RIGHTEOUSNESS.'

The act of faith has two sides: God's side and man's side, divine revelation and human response. Faith is man's positive response to God's revelation.

God's Side—Divine Revelation

All faith begins here. Before we can believe we must have a word from God. Examining Abraham's case we find a twofold revelation: of God's character and His will.

A Revelation of God's Character. Verse 17 describes God as the One 'who gives life to the dead and calls into being that which does not exist.' The character of God is the foundation of faith. You cannot trust someone you do not know. The Psalmist said, 'And those who know Thy name will put their trust in Thee' (Psalm 9:10). It is God's character that inspires our faith; if we know His name (His revealed character) we will trust Him.

Everything in the Christian life depends upon an adequate understanding of who God is. There is God as He is and there is God as we conceive Him to be. We do not worship God as He is but as we conceive Him to be. If our concept of God is wrong, our worship of Him will likewise be wrong. And an inadequate or inaccurate knowledge of God will result in a defective faith. As was pointed out in chapter four, those whom Jesus rebuked for their inferior faith had an inferior understanding of Jesus. The centurion's faith was superior because his knowledge of Jesus was superior. God's character inspires our faith, and before He asks us to trust Him, He reveals Himself (His character). His character defines and directs our trust.

An accurate knowledge of God is essential. Take the case of the Samaritan woman. As Jesus talked with her the conversation shifted to worship. She exposed her erroneous idea of worship when she said, 'Our fathers worshipped in this mountain; and you people say that in Jerusalem is the place where men ought to worship' (John 4:20). Jesus corrected her by saying, 'God is spirit; and those who worship Him must worship in spirit and truth' (John 4:24). Before He could set her straight on the nature of worship He first had to set her straight on the nature of God. God must be worshipped according to His nature. He is spirit; therefore, He must be worshipped in spirit. The nature of God determines the nature of worship.

The same principle is enunciated in 1 John. The apostle writes, he says, so that we may have fellowship with God; and, significantly, the first thing he discusses is the nature of God. 'And this is the message we have heard from Him and announce to you, that God is light, and in Him there is no darkness at all' (1 John 1:5). In the next verse he says, 'If we say that we have fellowship with Him and yet walk in the darkness, we lie and do not practice the truth; but if we walk in the light as He Himself is in the light, we have fellowship...' (1 John 1:6, 7). Our walk must correspond to His nature. God is light; therefore, we must walk in the light.

The life style of the believer is simply a response to the character of God. Peter writes, 'But like the Holy One who called you, be holy yourselves also in all your behaviour; because it is written, "YOU SHALL BE HOLY, FOR I AM HOLY" ' (1 Peter 1:15, 16). Why should Christians be holy? Because God is holy. No other reason is given. No other is needed.

Again the apostle John says, 'God is love, and the one who abides in love abides in God.... We love, because He first loved us' (1 John 4:16, 19). In chapter two he tells us that 'the one who says he abides in Him ought himself to walk in the same manner as He walked' (1 John 2:6).

And Christ said, 'Therefore you are to be perfect, as your heavenly Father is perfect' (Matthew 5:48).

Faith, then, is our response to the character of God. This demands an ever-deepening knowledge of God. Augustine prayed, 'Grant me, Lord, to know and understand which is first, to call on Thee or to praise Thee? And, again, to know Thee or to call on Thee. For who can call on Thee, not knowing Thee? For he that knoweth Thee not may call on Thee as other than Thou art.'

Spurgeon said, 'The proper study of the Christian is the Godhead. The highest science, the loftiest speculation, the mightiest philosophy, which can ever engage the attention of a child of God, is the name, the nature, the person, the work, the doings, and the existence of the great God whom he calls his Father.'

Paul wrote to the Philippians: 'I count all things to be loss in view of the surpassing value of knowing Christ Jesus my Lord, for whom I have suffered the loss of all things... that I may know Him' (Philippians 3:8, 10).

The Revelation Matches The Need

To Abraham, God revealed Himself as the One who 'gives life to the dead and calls into being that which does not exist.' Why did God reveal these particular attributes of His character? The answer lies in that for which Abraham had to believe God. God promised him two things: one, he and Sarah would have a son and; two, Abraham would become the father of many nations. But there was a slight problem. Sarah's womb was 'dead', and Abraham, being a hundred years old, was as good as dead. For them to produce a son would be like bringing life out of death. And, in the light of his physical infirmity, to call Abraham a father of many nations was to speak of something that did not exist.

Was it possible to believe such a thing could happen? What would Abraham base his faith on? The nature of God! Resurrection and creation are two of God's specialties. Do you see it? The revelation of God's character corresponded with His promise.

God gave to Abraham a staggering promise and at the same time gave him a revelation that would enable him to believe the promise. God made known to Abraham that part of His character that would inspire and enable Abraham to believe. The revelation matched the faith required. That's why I say that faith is based on the character of God; it is the human response to the divine revelation.

This principle is seen in Joshua's experience of faith. Faced with the herculean task of conquering Jericho, Joshua was confronted one day by a strange man with a sword in his hand. When asked who he was and what he was there for, the man answered, 'I indeed come now as captain of the host of the Lord' (Joshua 5:14). He then informed Joshua that he had already given the city into Joshua's hands and outlined the strategy for taking it. I believe, with most Bible scholars, that this was a preincarnate appearance of Christ; but whether it was or not, it constituted a revelation from God and formed the basis of Joshua's belief that the Lord had delivered Jericho into his hands. Note that the revelation corresponded to the required faith. Joshua had to believe God for a military victory; thus God revealed Himself, not as a shepherd or a guide, but as a Warrior.

The raising of Lazarus provides another example. Arriving in Bethany following the death of Lazarus, Jesus was immediately met by the dead man's sister, Martha, who said, 'Lord, if you had been here, my brother would not have died' (John 11:21). When

Jesus promised her that Lazarus would rise again, she replied, 'I know that he will rise again in the resurrection on the last day' (John 11:24). Like a good conservative evangelical she believed in the doctrine of the resurrection. But Jesus had something more immediate in mind. He wanted Martha to believe that Lazarus would be raised right then and there. To create that faith He said, 'I am the resurrection and the life' (John 11:25). The resurrection is more than a doctrine, Jesus was saying; it is a Person–and that Person is here, ready to restore your brother to life. Again, the revelation matched the faith needed.

So then, faith is first and foremost our response to the character of God.

A Revelation of God's Will. Romans 4:17, 18 says, '(As it is written, "A FATHER OF MANY NATIONS HAVE I MADE YOU")...in hope against hope he believed, in order that he might become a father of many nations, according to that which had been spoken, "SO SHALL YOUR DESCENDANTS BE." '

Observe the sequence. First, God told Abraham that He had made him a father of many nations; then, in response to that revelation, Abraham believed 'in order that he might become' what God had willed. Abraham's faith was linked to the will of God. And when his faith was united with God's purpose he became in fact what God said he was. It is imperative that we understand that faith operates only within the boundary of God's will. In other words, without a knowledge of God's will there can be no real faith. In prayer, for instance, we cannot ask *in faith* if we are guessing at the will of God. The prayer of faith is the prayer offered in the knowledge of that will; it is not shooting in the dark, hoping we'll get lucky and hit the bullseye. Faith is not man's way of getting his will done in heaven; it is God's way of getting His will done on earth.

Biblical faith, as we saw in chapter three, is a gift from God, and God will not grant us faith to believe something contrary to His will.

Give special attention again to the wording of the text. God said, 'I have made you a father of many nations,' and Abraham believed in order to become a father of many nations. By faith Abraham cooperated with the purpose of God. And that's the intent of faith: to enable us to cooperate with God. Have you ever noticed how much of our praying is actually an attempt to get God to cooperate with us?

We have this whole thing backwards. We investigate and deliberate, gather a consensus of opinion, call a committee meeting and come up with a plan of what needs to be done and how to do it—then we pray. And often what we're doing is trying to convince God our plan is a good one and to persuade Him to go along with it. We're trying to get God to believe in us, when He wants us to believe in Him; we're trying to get God to cooperate with our plan when He wants us to cooperate with His.

Faith doesn't pull God over to our side; it aligns us with Him and His purpose. God has not said, 'If you

have enough faith I will do whatever you wish.'
What He has said is, 'If you will put your faith in Me
I will enable you to do whatever I want.'

Man's Side – The Human Response

Revelation demands a response. God reveals truth,
not to satisfy our curiosity or to increase our store of
information, but that we might obey. Faith is the
positive response to God's revelation. It is man's
'Amen' to all that God has declared.

What does this positive response involve? What
are we to do? Since Abraham is our model, it is
reasonable to assume that the steps taken by him are
the ones to be taken by us.

1. Accept the Promise. 'In hope against hope he
believed' (v. 18). 'And being fully assured that what
He had promised, He was able also to perform' (v.
21). Hebrews 11:13 describes the faith of Abraham
and others like this:

> All these died in faith, without receiving the
> promises, but having seen them, and having
> welcomed them from a distance, and having
> confessed that they were strangers and exiles
> on the earth.

Concerning the promises of God, the writer says
that these saints *saw the promises* (that's revelation),
and then *welcomed the promises* (that's acceptance).

The Authorised Version says they 'embraced' them. The Greek word means 'to draw to oneself, to welcome as your own.' And that is what we must do with God's promise—draw it to us, take it in our arms and embrace it and say, 'This is mine.' Though the promise was first made 2,000 years ago, and millions of people have since claimed it, we are to embrace it as though we are the first and only ones to whom God made it.

One of the members of a church I pastored some years ago was a fine tailor. He asked me one Sunday if I had ever owned a tailor-made suit. When I told him I hadn't, he gave the suit I was wearing the once-over and said, 'You need one. Come to my shop tomorrow and we'll measure you.' A few weeks later I was wearing a beautiful, black, 100 per cent mohair tailor-made suit. Do you know what I liked best about that suit? On the inside of the coat, instead of a common brand label, were these words, stitched in red silk thread: 'Made exclusively for Ronald Dunn.' That's class.

But far more exciting than a tailor-made suit are tailor-made promises! And every promise carries this label: 'Made exclusively for Ronald Dunn.' That's grace.

Involved in our acceptance of the promise is a commitment to obey. Hebrews 11:8 says, 'By faith Abraham, when he was called, obeyed....' His obedience was the evidence of his faith. Believing God always expresses itself in unhesitating obedience. The fourth chapter of John's Gospel relates the incident of a royal official who begged Jesus to come to his house and heal his dying son. Instead of returning with the man to his home, Jesus said, 'Go your way; your son lives' (John 4:50). There was the divine revelation: a promise ('Your son lives') and a command ('Go your way'). If the father refused to go back home without Jesus it would indicate unbelief. Belief and obedience are inseparably linked together. The Bible says, 'The man believed the word that Jesus spoke to him, and he started off' (John 4:50). Accepting the promise of Jesus, he obeyed.

Because obedience is so vital to faith, a full chapter will be devoted to it later.

One more important point. Romans 4 contains one of the great secrets of faith. Look at the last phrase of verse 16 and the first part of verse 17: '...Abraham, who is the father of us all...in the sight of Him whom He believed.' In the sight of God, Abraham was already the father of many nations. When God looked at Abraham He saw him surrounded by offspring. Why, it would have been easier to count the stars in the sky than to number Abraham's descendants. That's how God saw Abraham. And Abraham accepted God's viewpoint; he saw himself as God saw him.

Seeing things as God sees them is, I believe, the secret of a living, victorious faith. We must see ourselves as God sees us; we must look at life through the eyes of God. And, you know, things look a lot better from up there! From up there the devil looks defeated, my sins are nowhere in sight, every need is supplied, and all problems solved.

2. Renounce All Confidence in Human Resources.

Read it again. I didn't say to renounce human resources, only our *confidence* in them. The difference is important, as we will see. But first, look at Romans 4:18: 'In hope against hope he believed.' The first 'hope' refers to Abraham's confidence in God's promise; the second to his confidence in his own ability. His confidence in God was in direct opposition to any confidence in the flesh.

Well, of course. What choice did he have, being a hundred years old? That's just the point. Remember Ishmael? He was Abraham's contribution to God's redemptive programme, a product of confidence in his ability to help out God. Perhaps it was to prevent another Ishmael that God waited until Abraham was impotent with age to fulfil the promise. This time there would be no doubt that God alone did it, and God alone would receive the glory. If we are unwilling to renounce human confidence, God may have to renounce it for us. Faith not only trusts God, it distrusts human abilities.

Occasionally I receive a letter from the pastor at a place where I'm to speak. It goes something like this: 'We're going to have the greatest meeting in the history of our church, of this town! We have seventy-three committees working around the clock; we've mailed invitations to every residence in the city; your picture is printed on every grocery sack used at the supermarket; we've stretched a banner across Main Street; and the day before the meeting starts an aeroplane is going to drop 100,000 pink leaflets over the city. We can't miss!' But we do. Sometimes God must let us fail rather than allow us to take the credit for something He did.

Don't misunderstand. Faith doesn't renounce the *use* of human resources, only *confidence* in them. Abraham *did* father a son and Sarah *did* give birth to him. There's no record of God delivering Isaac from heaven in a cloud. He used the human apparatus He had created for that very purpose. But while Abraham and Sarah became parents by a very natural and human process, neither of them took credit for what happened. The glory—and the credit—went to God.

I believe we ought to use every available resource—personally, I think the supermarket grocery bags is a great idea—but we must never place our confidence in those things. We will never have faith in God's ability until we renounce all faith in our own.

3. Face the Problem but Focus on the Promise. Paul continues his description of Abraham's faith in verses 19 and 20: 'And without becoming weak in faith he contemplated his own body, now as good as dead since he was about a hundred years old, and the deadness of Sarah's womb; yet, with respect to the promise of God, he did not waver in unbelief, but grew strong in faith, giving glory to God.'

Abraham did not shut his eyes to the impossibility of his situation. The Bible says he considered it.

Considered is a strong Greek verb indicating a careful consideration resulting in a clear understanding. He didn't just glance at the problem; he looked it squarely in the eye, studying the situation until he fully understood the predicament. And he did it without becoming weak in faith.

You don't have to hide the facts from faith. Faith does not fear contradicting circumstances. To the contrary, true faith becomes stronger when confronted with impossibilities.

But the opposite seems to be true of many modern saints. Our present-day faith is easily intimidated by discouraging facts. Like Gideon we cry, 'If the Lord is with us, why then has all this happened to us?' (Judges 6:13). We are outclassed by Abraham, who could calmly consider insurmountable problems 'without becoming weak in faith' or 'wavering in unbelief.'

What was the secret of his faith? Look again at verse 20. 'Yet, with respect to the promise of God, he did not waver in unbelief.' The key is the phrase, 'with respect to the promise of God'; it is emphasized in the Greek text in order to stress that upon which Abraham's faith was focused. The American Standard Version of 1901 reads, 'yet, looking unto the promise of God.' While examining the problem, Abraham kept his eyes glued to the promise of God. He was so absorbed in the promise, he was not threatened by the problem.

Spurgeon said, 'Look at yourself and your doubts will increase. Look at Jesus and they will disappear.'

Like Peter, if we take our eyes off Jesus we will sink beneath the waves of doubt.

Naturally, we would prefer an unchallenged faith. But faith, like gold that perishes, must be put to the test (1 Peter 1:7). An untried faith is a worthless faith. It is the trial that determines the authenticity of our faith. Face it, your faith will be tested; it will be challenged by critics and contradicted by circumstances. And the only anchor that can hold you in place is the promise of God. Look at the problems—but make your last and longest look at the promise.

Before we leave this point, let me say a word about *doubt*. These verses do not imply that Abraham was totally free of any inward conflict. It is difficult to imagine that not a single doubt passed through his mind. I agree with Calvin, who said, 'The mind is never so enlightened that there are no remains of ignorance, nor the heart so established that there are no misgivings. With these evils of our nature faith maintains a perpetual conflict, in which conflict it is often sorely shaken and put to great stress; but still it conquers.' William Sanday, in his classic work on Romans, translates the phrase, 'And yet with the promise in view no impulse of unbelief made him hesitate.'[2] Certainly there were the 'impulses of unbelief'; but with his eyes fixed on the promise, his faith triumphed over all the difficulties.

Don't let doubts make you doubt. With the father of the demon-possessed boy, cry, 'Lord, I believe; help thou mine unbelief' (Mark 9:24, AV).

4. Rest on God's Faithfulness. Abraham's act of faith reaches its climax with these words: 'He...grew strong in faith, giving glory to God, and being fully assured that what He had promised, He was able also to perform' (Romans 4:20, 21). As a result of keeping his eyes on the promise, Abraham grew strong in faith; this strengthening of his faith was expressed by his assurance that God would keep His word, and by giving glory to God.

In other words, Abraham, having accepted God's promise and having acted upon it, left the matter with God, counting on His faithfulness.

Abraham's faith did not weaken when he contemplated the deadness of his body because he knew the condition of his body had nothing whatsoever to do with the outcome. It wasn't Abraham's performance that mattered—it was God's. After all, it was God who made the promise, not Abraham.

Isaac was God's idea. Abraham did not promise God he would produce a son for the purpose of redeeming the world. That was God's promise; therefore, it was God's responsibility.

Again, we have things backwards. We are constantly making promises to God and trying to keep them. And if we promise, then we must perform. And that would make anyone, even Abraham, waver in unbelief. We have not promised God we will supply all our needs—*He* has promised to supply all our needs. We have not promised God we will overcome the world—that's His promise to us. It is

God, not man, who has promised to remove the mountains that block our path.

It is this simple: if you make a promise, it's up to you to keep it. If God makes a promise, the responsibility is His. And what God has promised He will perform.

He will perform. Often we try to keep God's promises for Him. What is Ishmael but Abraham's attempt to fulfil God's promise? Faith is believing that what God has promised He can and will do. If God has promised, *He* will perform. Only believe.

> Faith, simple faith, the promise sees
> And looks to God alone;
> Laughs at impossibilities
> And cries, 'It shall be done.'

The issue of such assurance is 'giving glory to God.' To give glory to God means to openly acknowledge Him as God, ascribing to Him all honour and praise and credit. We glorify God when we believe He will do what He has promised and demonstrate that belief by our actions. Sanday renders the phrase, 'He gave praise to God for the miracle that was to be wrought in him.'[3] Abraham thanked God in advance for what was to happen. He acted as though the child had already been born.

Faith and praise are inseparable; where you find one you will find the other, supporting and strengthening each other. Faith makes praise shout, and when faith hears the shout of praise it in turn grows stronger and bolder. Praise is the protector of faith, for it is praise that silences the accusing voice of doubt. Learn the art of praise. It is the highest expression of our faith in God.

So there stands our model of faith, Abraham, believing in spite of the facts and giving thanks before the fact. And when we believe as he believed, we will receive as he received.

Notes

1. William Sanday and A. C. Headlam, *The Epistle to the Romans* (New York: Charles Scribner's Sons, 1901), p. 113.
2. *Ibid.*
3. *Ibid.*

CHAPTER NINE

Does Confession Bring Possession?

'Asingle word has sometimes lost or won an empire.' When George James wrote those words in *Richelieu* he was nearer biblical truth than he realized. For many Christians, an empire of heavenly blessings has been lost or won because of their words–or lack of them.

While the practice of confession is often abused and misused, there is in the Bible a persistent link between believing and speaking. And while there is more to biblical confession than simply 'naming it and claiming it,' it is true the inward act of believing must often manifest itself by the outward act of speaking. Confession is faith turned inside out; it is both a sign of the reality of faith and the inevitable product of it.

This bond between faith and confession is emphasized by Jesus in Mark 11:23: 'For verily I say unto you, That whosoever shall *say* unto this mountain, Be thou removed, and be thou cast into the sea; and shall not doubt in his heart, but shall believe that those things which he *saith* shall come to pass; he shall have whatsoever he *saith*' (AV, emphasis added). Notice that Jesus does not say, 'He shall have whatsoever he believes,' but, 'He shall have whatsoever he *says*.' Confession and faith are two sides of the same coin, and it is the confession of the mouth that releases the belief of the heart.

This same idea is expressed by Paul in Romans 10:9, 10: 'That if you confess with your mouth Jesus as Lord, and believe in your heart that God raised Him from the dead, you shall be saved; for with the heart man believes, resulting in righteousness, and with the mouth he confesses, resulting in salvation.' Believing in the heart and confessing with the mouth are both essential with regard to salvation. The belief in the heart must be and inevitably is confessed with the mouth. Commenting on this verse, John Murray says, 'Confession without faith would be vain.... But likewise faith without confession would be shown to be spurious.'[1]

This essential link between confession and faith appears also in Matthew 17:19, 20. Explaining why His disciples were unable to deliver a demon-possessed boy, Jesus said, 'Because of the littleness of your faith; for truly I say to you, if you have faith as a mustard seed, you shall say to this mountain, "Move from here to there," and it shall move; and nothing shall be impossible to you.'

And again in Luke 17:6, Jesus said, 'If you had faith like a mustard seed, you would say to this mulberry tree, "Be uprooted and be planted in the sea"; and it would obey you.'

None of these statements can be restricted only to prayer. The words of which Jesus spoke are not words of prayer. When we pray we speak to God;

here we are told to speak to a mountain and a tree. I
can't remember the last time I prayed to a mountain
or a tree—I can't remember a first time. While these
promises can be applied to prayer, they are not
limited to it. Here Jesus is revealing the phenomenal
power of faith when translated into words. And what
is even more significant, the act of speaking to a tree
or a mountain is not presented as bizarre or extraordinary. On the contrary, *not* to express such belief
would be abnormal. As Paul says in 2 Corinthians
4:13 (AV), 'We also believe, and therefore speak.'
According to Jesus, merely believing in the heart
that the mountain will move is sometimes not
enough. What is in the heart must be expressed by
the mouth. Norman Grubb is right when he calls
confession 'the summit of faith.'[2]

The Prominence And Power Of Words

Throughout the Bible, words occupy a place of surprising prominence. God created the world by the
power of His spoken word. Hebrews 11:3 tells us that
the worlds 'were prepared by the word of God.' And
in Psalm 33:6 we read, 'By the word of the Lord the
heavens were made, and by the breath of His mouth
all their host.' Verse 9 says, 'For He spoke, and it
was done; He commanded, and it stood fast.' The
unifying thread running through the creation story
is, 'And God said.'

Not only was the world created by the word of
God, it is sustained by that same word. Jesus

'upholds all things by the word of His power' (Hebrews 1:3). In 2 Peter 3:5, 7 it says 'that by the word of God the heavens existed long ago and the earth was formed out of water and by water.... But the present heavens and earth by His word are being reserved.'

Jesus underscored the awesome importance of words when He said that whoever *speaks a word* against the Holy Spirit shall never be forgiven (Matthew 12:32). It is also worth noting that our Lord always rebuked Satan with spoken words. He cast out demons, not with thoughts, but with words. Paul dealt with the evil spirits that possessed the young slave girl at Philippi, not with thoughts or silent prayer, but by speaking directly to the spirit (Acts 16:18).

One of the most striking examples of the power of words is found in Matthew 12. Addressing the Pharisees, Jesus said, 'You brood of vipers, how can you, being evil, speak what is good? For the mouth speaks out of that which fills the heart. The good man out of his good treasure brings forth what is good; and the evil man out of his evil treasure brings forth what is evil. And I say to you, that every careless word that men shall speak, they shall render account for it in the day of judgment. For by your words you shall be justified, and by your words you shall be condemned' (Matthew 12:34–37).

It is 'out of that which fills the heart' that men speak. The mouth is like an overflow pipe. It reveals, not merely what is in the heart, but what *fills* the heart, what possesses and dominates the heart. This is why confession is strategic. When we speak we raise the curtain of our heart, exposing its contents. Our confession gives proof of our faith—or our lack of it.

When young David volunteered to fight Goliath, he told Saul, 'The Lord who delivered me from the paw of the lion and from the paw of the bear, He will deliver me from the hand of this Philistine' (1 Samuel 17:37). That was a confession of faith. Armed with five smooth stones and his sling, David marched right up to Goliath, looked him straight in the kneecaps, and declared, 'This day the Lord will deliver you up into my hands...that all the earth may know that there is a God in Israel' (1 Samuel 17:46). While the army of Israel confessed fear and defeat, David confessed victory.

When God instructed Abraham to take Isaac to Moriah and offer him as a sacrifice, Abraham obeyed. The writer of Hebrews reports that Abraham did this by faith, believing that, 'God is able to raise men even from the dead; from which he also received him back as a type' (Hebrews 11:19). This faith he expressed by his words; to his servants he said, 'Stay here with the donkey, and I and the lad will go yonder; and we will worship and return to you' (Genesis 22:5). To Isaac, who asked about the lamb for the sacrifice, he said, 'God will provide for Himself the lamb for the burnt offering' (Genesis 22:8).

Listen to Paul's confession of faith. In chapter

three I referred to his never-a-dull-minute excursion to Rome. At the darkest hour, when it looked as if they would all perish in the raging sea, the man of God appeared in the midst of the terrified crowd to tell them he had received assurance from God that all would be saved. Then came the words of confession: 'Therefore, keep up your courage, men, for I believe God, that it will turn out exactly as I have been told' (Acts 27:25).

Many more examples are available–Moses at the Red Sea, Gideon before the Midianites, Elijah on Mount Carmel. Always the faith that is in the heart is expressed by the words of the mouth.

Observe the chronology of believing in Hebrews 11:13, 14: 'All these died in faith, without receiving the promises, but having seen them, and having welcomed them from a distance, and having confessed that they were strangers and exiles on the earth. For those who say such things make it clear that they are seeking a country of their own.' These pilgrims of faith

SAW THE PROMISES,
    WELCOMED THE PROMISES,
        CONFESSED THE PROMISES.

God had promised them a city whose Builder and Maker was the Lord. On the basis of that promise they believed that this world was not their home; they were just passing through. By confessing that they were strangers and exiles on the earth they made it clear to those around that they believed God.

Why Confession?

I am not presuming to lay down any hard and fast rules regarding the exercise of faith, saying you must do it this way. There are no such rules. But I believe there are occasions when the effective exercise of faith will require confession. Here's why.

1. Confession Confirms the Reality of Our Faith. Remember what Jesus said: 'The mouth speaks out of that which fills the heart.' When the heart is full the mouth will speak. Our confession reveals whether our heart is totally committed and fully believing. One could almost say that there is a sense in which it is not genuine faith until it is confessed. This is certainly true with regard to saving faith.

2. Confession Cements Our Commitment to Trust God. Without a confession of our faith our commitment may be only a halfhearted commitment, one we can easily back out of. And make no mistake about it—we will be tempted to back out of it. Faith will be tested. Circumstances will contradict what God has said. Even our friends may intimidate our faith with discouraging words and negative attitudes. The light at the end of the tunnel may turn out to be a train. And if we have kept our faith hidden in our heart, it will be easier to succumb to the temptation to cast away our confidence and hedge our bets with the arm of flesh.

But if that faith has been paraded out of the closet and placed on the display shelf of confession we will find ourselves agreeing with Ezra. Ezra, you remember, was the man who led the exiles back to Jerusalem after being released from Babylonian captivity. Because of the many dangers along the way, he proclaimed a time of prayer and fasting to seek the Lord for a safe journey.

His reason for doing this makes interesting reading: 'For I was ashamed to request from the king troops and horsemen to protect us from the enemy on the way, because we had said to the king, "The hand of our God is favourably disposed to all those who seek Him, but His power and His anger are against all those who forsake Him" ' (Ezra 8:22). Ezra's confession locked him in! Had he not voiced his faith in front of the king he might have yielded to the temptation to prop it up with the king's army.

After all, it's easier to trust God when you have an army backing you up. But you can't go around boasting to the king about how powerful your God is and then ask for military aid. Ezra's confession stabilized him and he did not waver in the hour of testing.

Speaking our faith settles and seals it. Confession is a commitment made, a bridge burned, a flag raised, a vote cast, an oath taken, a contract signed, an issue decided.

3. Confession Focuses Our Attention on God and His

Promises. Confession directs our thoughts away from ourselves and centres them upon Christ and His faithfulness, preventing us from becoming introspective. Often after making a commitment of faith we find ourselves travelling through a period of darkness when our senses fail to register any signs of God's presence. Doubts arise; our faith becomes fragile. Confession is a weapon of warfare that enables us to destroy the stronghold of doubt and 'every lofty thing raised up against the knowledge of God...taking every thought captive to the obedience of Christ' (2 Corinthians 10:5). This is a good way of following Paul's advice in Philippians 4:8, 'Finally, brethren, whatever is true, whatever is honourable, whatever is right, whatever is pure, whatever is lovely, whatever is of good repute, if there is any excellence and if anything worthy of praise, let your mind dwell on these things.'

4. Confession Encourages Others to Believe. This is the whole point of Hebrews 11. The believers to whom the author writes are going through a severe trial. Their faith is being tested; some are wavering. Encouragement is needed. The author reminds them of others like Abraham and Moses, who endured great trials and who, by faith, emerged victorious. After parading these heroes of faith before their memory, he says, 'Therefore, since we have so great a cloud of witnesses surrounding us...let us run with endurance the race that is set before us' (Hebrews 12:1). When he speaks of a cloud of witnesses surrounding them, he does not mean that people in heaven are looking down to watch us run. They are not spectators but testifiers. The thought is that the testimonies of Abraham and the others will serve as encouragement, challenging them to believe God and remain steadfast.

There is a beautiful touch in the account of Paul and Silas in the Philippian jail. After beating them, the jailer throws them into the inner prison and binds them with stocks. And then Scripture says, 'But about midnight Paul and Silas were praying and singing hymns of praise to God, and the prisoners were listening to them' (Acts 16:25). *And the prisoners were listening to them!* In the midnight trials of our souls, the prisoners are always listening to us. And what they hear will either encourage or discourage them to believe.

5. Confession Glorifies God. Psalm 50:23 tells us that, 'Whoso offereth praise glorifieth me' (AV), and the confession of faith is one of the highest forms of praise. The word 'confess' means to *say the same thing*, and in confession we are simply saying the same thing God has said, affirming our faith in His Word. What could please God more than hearing his children boldly voice their faith in their heavenly Father?

When my son was about ten years old, I chauffeured him and one of his friends to a party at the church. They were riding in the back seat, having, of all things, a big theological discussion. Turning down the radio so I could eavesdrop on this phenomenon, I overheard my son drive home a point by repeating almost word for word something I had said in a sermon the Sunday before. I was surprised and delighted—surprised that he had listened carefully enough to remember the phrase so accurately; and delighted that he had adopted it as his own conviction. It was a special joy to hear my words coming from the mouth of my son. Surely God must experience a similar joy when He hears His words coming back to Him from the lips of His believing children.

Cautions Concerning Confession

I have observed among many Christians a tendency to turn the principle of confession into something magical or physical. Like many biblical truths, confession may be driven to the point of excess and becomes totally unbiblical. Misunderstood and misused confession may become a yoke of bondage. Let me mention three ways in which this can happen.

1. A Magic Formula. One night after an exhausting preaching service I climbed into the car of a friend and collapsed in the back seat. 'Man, I am bushed,' I groaned. Instantly my friend whirled around, pointed his finger at me, and said, 'Don't say that! That's a negative confession.' I thought it a rather honest confession; I *was* bushed. Frankly, I've been around some well-meaning souls who have so twisted this idea that, had they been present at the crucifixion, I'm convinced that when Jesus cried out, 'I thirst,' they would have rebuked Him for making a negative confession.

A 'bad' or 'negative' confession is confessing something contrary to what God has said, and God has not said that we would be immune to physical exhaustion. Even Jesus grew weary and needed rest and refreshment.

The wife of a preacher I know was invited to a covered-dish luncheon at a neighbouring church. When she walked in with her culinary contribution, one of the ladies asked what she had brought.

'Devilled eggs,' she said.

Immediately the woman flung out her hands and said, 'I bind that in the name of Jesus!'

Unperturbed, the preacher's wife said, 'You can bind it all you want, it's still devilled eggs.'

While our words are important, they are not magic. Merely confessing something doesn't make it so. Remember, confession doesn't create faith; faith creates confession.

Prevalent today is the 'name it and claim it' syndrome – the idea that you will have whatever you say (literally), even if you don't mean what you say. A casually spoken word, even, can result in either a curse or a blessing, depending on what you said. If you confess good things, good things will happen to you; if you confess bad things, bad things will happen to you. You have whatever you say.

The 'name it and claim it' folk believe that if you confess wealth, you will be wealthy; if you confess health, you will be healthy. Some go so far as to say that if you casually say, 'I'm afraid I'll have cancer someday,' you at that moment give the devil authority, which before he did not have, to give you cancer. Saying something negative, according to this view, actually puts you under a curse of words and gives Satan the right to do whatever you have said. You must, therefore, be careful at all times of what you say.

To live under such a bondage is both unhealthy and unscriptural. Only as our confession reflects the revealed will of God does it have validity. Such power is vested, not in *our* words by in the Word of God, confessed and obeyed.

And then there have been some fever-ridden folk who, between their sneezes and coughs, kept saying, 'I'm healed, I'm healed.' When I questioned the fever and the sneezing and the coughing, I was told these things were just symptoms. They were healed, they explained, but the symptoms remained, and unless they held fast their confession of healing, the illness would return. I have no desire to make light of such sincerity, but I fail to see the value of a healing that leaves you suffering with the symptoms. It was not that way in the biblical healings. All the healings in the Bible were complete—the symptoms never stayed around once the disease left. I believe this is a case of assigning to the mere act of confession a power that God has not given it and that it borders on superstition.

2. *Priming the Pump*. Teachers of faith often tell us that when we are believing God for something specific we should confess it to someone else. If I am trusting God for one hundred dollars I ought to tell someone what I am believing God for. And there are instances in which this should be done. But our confession may become a subtle way of priming the pump. I may find myself choosing to make my confession to a wealthy friend, hoping he will 'feel led' to supply the money. That would encourage my faith more than making my confession to a beggar. As someone has said, 'We have not because we hint not.'

I pastored a large and very generous church and I'm certain that if I confessed to the members one Sunday morning that I was believing God for a new suit, I would have had it before the day was out. I'm not saying that is wrong, but for me to use that as an example of faith and of the power of confession would be wrong, because not everyone has a large congregation eager to satisfy his needs. We preachers have an advantage that others do not have and we must be careful about making our particular experience the standard for others.

A good rule of confession is this: Make your confession to someone who cannot fulfil your request.

3. *Positive Thinking*. The line between psychic power and spiritual power is almost imperceptible and the two are easily confused. Psychic power is often mistaken for spiritual power. We're all familiar

with the story of the fellow who arrives at the office feeling great, but after a few scheming friends tell him he looks bad, he goes home sick. The concentration of the mind does often determine the direction of the life; and faith has sometimes been defined as psychic power channelled in good and godly directions. But that is not biblical faith. The confession of faith is not a mind-over-matter proposition.

This is, I think, the mistake often made about positive thinking. Again I want to emphasize that I am not criticizing positive thinking as such. Everyone ought to possess a positive mental attitude; I hate to be around someone with a negative mental attitude. But again, positive thinking is not biblical faith.

Positive thinking says, 'Believe and it will be so.'

Biblical faith says, 'Believe because God has said it is so.'

Positive thinking is based on our own desires—if we believe hard enough we will get what we want. Faith is based upon God's desire for us as revealed in His word.

Positive thinking is in the end merely believing in yourself. Biblical faith is repudiating all confidence in the flesh and believing in the Lord.

Norman Grubb offers this word of caution concerning confession:

> The word of faith, if a mere word, can be a shallow sham. Faith is *the whole man in action*, and the word of faith includes the heart and

mind that is in tune with the will of God and His written revelation, the voice that speaks the word of faith, and all subsequent action that is in full conformity with the position of faith which has been declared.[3]

What, Then, Are We To Confess?

We are to confess three things: we are to confess that

WE ARE WHAT GOD SAYS WE ARE...
WE HAVE WHAT GOD SAYS WE HAVE...
WE CAN DO WHAT GOD SAYS WE CAN DO.

Remember: confession is agreeing with God, saying the same thing He has said. That which we confess must be that which God has already spoken to us. This eliminates the idea that if I want something, all I need do is confess it and I will have whatever I say. As already noted, confession does not create faith; faith creates confession. The idea originates with God, not with us.

Biblical faith is imparted to us by God through His word—the external Word of the Bible and the internal word of the Spirit. We must *first* have a word from God. And it is this point that many miss. In their fervent rush to use the newly discovered key of faith they forget that it unlocks only those doors God has made—not the doors created by our wishes.

But don't despair. There are riches enough behind God's doors of grace to satisfy the longing of every heart. He still opens His hand to satisfy the desire of every creature. And once we begin to explore the treasures those doors conceal we will thank God for not abandoning us to the fool's gold of our own capricious desires.

Notes

1. John Murray, *The Epistle to the Romans, Volume II* (Grand Rapids: Wm. B. Eerdmans Publishing Co., 1965), p. 56.
2. Norman Grubb, *The Law of Faith* (Ft. Washington: Christian Literature Crusade, 1947), p. 112. Taken from copyrighted material used by permission of the Christian Literature Crusade, Fort Washington, PA 19034.
3. *Ibid.*, p. 116.

CHAPTER TEN

How to Complete
Your Faith

The goal of faith is to turn the things promised into the things possessed. And once we realize the immeasurable wealth contained in God's promises, no sacrifice will be too great, no discipline too severe, for faith to reach its goal. This is the pearl of great price and we will be willing to sell all else in order to possess it. But, unfortunately, the faith of many Christians never reaches its goal. Like exhausted runners, they find their faith collapses just short of the finish line. More than a few once-eager souls have said to me, 'Well, I tried faith, but it didn't work for me.'

But the problem is many of these discouraged believers did not *complete* their faith. For faith to reach its goal, it must be completed. What do I mean by 'completing your faith'? The epistle of James uses this phrase in describing the faith of Abraham.

Was not Abraham our father justified by works, when he offered up Isaac his son on the altar? You see that faith was working with his works, and as a result of the works, faith was perfectly [*completed*, marginal reading]; and the Scripture was fulfilled which says, 'AND

167

ABRAHAM BELIEVED GOD, AND IT WAS RECK-
ONED TO HIM AS RIGHTEOUSNESS,' and he was
called the friend of God (James 2:21-23).

Let's take a closer look at the phrase 'faith was
perfected.' The word translated *perfect* means 'to
bring to an end, to accomplish, to bring to maturity,
to fulfil its purpose.' Charles B. Williams in his translation renders the phrase, 'faith was made complete.'
The Beck translation is especially vivid: '...reached
its goal.'

Perfected faith is faith that has reached its goal,
faith that has accomplished its purpose. It has completed the task assigned it. Abraham's goal was to be
righteous before God. The task assigned to his faith
was to obtain righteousness–and it completed its
task.

But how? What did Abraham do to perfect his
faith? James gives the answer in these words: 'Was
not Abraham our father justified by works, when he
offered up Isaac his son on the altar? You see that
faith was working with his works, *and as a result of
the works, faith was perfected*' (vv. 21, 22, emphasis
added).

Faith is perfected, or completed, by works. Abraham's experience is Exhibit A in James' argument
concerning faith and works. This argument, beginning with verse 14 of chapter two, describes two men
who claim to have faith. But only one claim is legiti-
mate. One man has faith (so he says) and the other

has faith plus something else—works. James asserts that the latter is the genuine article.

The faith versus works issue is a controversy familiar to all students of the New Testament. Some argue that when James says we are justified by works as well as by faith, he is contradicting Paul, who teaches that we are justified by faith alone (Romans 3:28). Paul plainly states that Abraham was justified by faith without works.

But no real conflict exists between Paul and James. While both use the same word, they attach different meanings to it. For instance, when Paul speaks of 'work' he is referring to the keeping of the Jewish ceremonial law. But James has in mind the everyday good works of the Christian, which, according to the apostle, are the product and proof of salvation. Again, when Paul talks of being justified, he means our righteous standing before God, our having been declared righteous by God.

But James uses the term in the sense of vindication, being *seen to be righteous* by those who observe our behaviour. In other words, Paul is referring to our justification before God, and James to our justification before men. God sees our faith and because of it declares us to be righteous. But men can see our faith only when it is recast in the form of good works.

James says, 'But someone may well say, "You have faith, and I have works; show me your faith without the works, and I will show you my faith by my works" ' (James 2:18). Genuine faith always identifies itself by works. If there are no works, there is no faith. Faith without works is but a hollow profession, and works without faith nothing but sterile activity. What breath is to the body, works are to faith. If, James says, a man claims to have faith but there is no visible evidence, no good works issuing from his life, his claim is false.

The Bible is uncompromisingly clear on this point. Faith without works is dead, able to accomplish nothing. If it is to reach its goal, faith must work. These verses suggest two kinds of works necessary to complete our faith.

Cooperating Works

'You see that faith co-operated with his good deeds, and by his good deeds faith was made complete' (James 2:22, Williams Translation).

Faith expresses itself in works. Faith and works have often been seen as antagonists, two opposing qualities between which we must choose. Those who choose works often accuse the faith-folk of laziness and indifference. Those who side with faith sometimes accuse the work-folk of labouring in the energy of the flesh. But the two are not mutually exclusive. They are part and parcel of each other, and to separate one from the other destroys them both. J. B. Phillips gives a good description of this in his translation: 'Can't you see that his faith and his actions were, so to speak, *partners*...?' (emphasis added). I like to think of the relationship between faith and works as 'Faith and Son, Incorporated'—and the son's name is Works.

True faith is active. Read again the account of the faith of the Old Testament saints in Hebrews 11. The writer describes their faith by talking about their works. They *did something*. Believing God does not mean lounging lazily about with our arms folded and 'letting God do it.' Faith is acting on the revealed will of God.

To believe God is to obey God. In Hebrews 3:18, 19, the writer, speaking of Israel's failure to enter the Promised Land, says, 'And to whom did He swear that they should not enter His rest, but to those who were disobedient? And so we see that they were not able to enter because of unbelief.' In verse 18 he says they could not enter because of disobedience; in verse 19 the reason given is unbelief.

Well, which was it—disobedience or unbelief? It was both. Disobedience and unbelief are two sides of the same coin. Disobedience *is* unbelief. Regardless of how loudly we may claim to believe the Bible, we believe only as much of it as we obey.

When was Abraham justified? At what precise point was his faith completed and credited to his account as righteousness? 'Was not Abraham our father justified by works, *when he offered up Isaac his son on the altar*? (James 2:21, emphasis added). Abraham's faith reached its goal when he did exactly as God had commanded.

One of our major problems is *reversed responsibilities*. By this I mean that we often try to get God to do our part while we attempt to do His. For example, take a common approach to evangelism. Many Christians, especially preachers, feel it is their responsibility to produce evangelistic results, and they measure their success by how many people they win to Christ. Don't get me wrong—I believe witnessing for Christ and winning others to saving faith in Him is the responsibility of every believer. I'm convinced one of the greatest sins of the modern church is its failure to share the gospel of Christ on a one-to-one basis.

But sometimes in our eagerness to have converts we stoop to gimmicks and psychological tricks, or we weaken the demands of the gospel to make it easy for reluctant repentants. And as a result, many of the converts listed on church rolls are there, not by the power of God, but through the persuasive cleverness of man. As Paul puts it, their faith stands in the wisdom of man rather than in the power of God (1 Corinthians 2:5).

Such an approach trespasses on God's responsibility. It is God who causes the growth (1 Corinthians 3:6, 7). Man can plough, plant, and water, but only God can give the increase.

But man has a responsibility. He must plant and water. God has promised to give the increase, but we must cooperate with Him by planting and watering. God will not plant and water—that is our responsibility. But, regrettably, many of us leave to God that which is our clear duty.

Let's imagine that we are driving through a rural

area and we stop at a farmhouse. Sitting on the front porch, rocking slowly back and forth in an ancient rocker, is the farmer.

'What are you doing?' we ask.

'Farming,' he says.

'What are you growing?'

'Wheat.'

But as we look out over his fields we see nothing but unploughed and unplanted ground. 'Excuse us, sir,' we say, 'but you haven't ploughed your fields. And it doesn't look like you've planted any wheat.'

'Yes, that's right.'

'We don't understand.'

'I'm farming by faith. Believing God for a crop.'

'But,' we protest, 'shouldn't you be *doing* something—maybe planting some wheat?'

'I *am* doing something,' he says.

'What?'

'I'm praying. Praying and believing. Praise the Lord!'

If every farmer exercised that kind of faith we would all have starved to death long ago. But that is no more ridiculous than some of the ideas about faith floating around. There is something we must do. Abiding in the Lord is not *idling* in the Lord. Faith must express itself by working.

Faith encourages us to work. The farmer doesn't plough his fields and plant his crops because he *hopes* something will come of it; he ploughs and plants because he *knows* something will come of his labour. Nor do we go out to the field of service to toil and labour, *hoping* something will happen. We work because we *know* something will happen. Just as the farmer has faith in the laws of sowing and reaping, we have faith in the promises of God.

A Christian shares the gospel with others because he has faith in the Word of God and in the operation of the Holy Spirit and knows that his labour in the Lord is not in vain. Going back to Paul's words in 1 Corinthians 3:6, 7: one man plants, another waters, but God gives the increase. And that is what encourages us to plant and water. Faith says, 'God *will* cause the growth. Regardless of how barren things may appear, God is faithful and will bless the planting and the watering.' Faith encourages us to do our part and trust God to do His.

Corresponding Works

'Now what use is it, my brothers, for a man to say he 'has faith' if his actions do not *correspond* with it?' (James 2:14, Phillips Translation, emphasis added). To illustrate his point, James tells of a brother who is naked and destitute of food. Seeing his need, we speak a word of faith, 'Go in peace, be warmed and filled.' And that is all we do. Now James says that kind of faith is dead. Unless we do something practical about the situation, our so-called faith is a mockery.

OK, so we must do something practical to show our faith. What shall we do? Paint the church? Sing a hymn? Preach a sermon on world hunger? None of these things would alleviate the man's suffering. It is not enough to do something; we must do something that corresponds to his need. In other words, James says, we ought to give him the things he needs; give him some food and clothing. That is corresponding works.

If a farmer really believes in the laws of sowing and reaping, he doesn't say, 'I'll go to Africa as a missionary and that will cultivate my fields.' If he believes in sowing and reaping, he will sow and reap.

For every act of faith there is a corresponding work. For example, Hebrews 11:9 tells us that Abraham believed that God would raise Isaac from the dead. Now what was the corresponding work that cooperated with his faith? To sacrifice Isaac as God commanded.

Rahab the harlot believed God would enable Israel to conquer Jericho. What was her corresponding work that cooperated with her faith? She hid the two spies from the king's men and helped them escape from the city. She switched rather than fought.

God told Joshua He would part the flooding waters of the Jordan River so all Israel could cross on dry ground. But the Jordan was sort of like one of those electric-eye doors at the supermarket—you must step toward it before it will open. Scripture says that 'when those who carried the ark came into the Jordan, and the feet of the priests carrying the ark were dipped in the edge of the water... that the waters which were flowing down from above stood and rose up in one heap... while all Israel crossed on dry ground' (Joshua 3:15-17). The waters parted (faith reached its goal) when the priests, in obedience to God's command, stepped into the water. That was the corresponding work that cooperated with their faith.

The application to present-day faith is inescapable. Are you facing a Jordan River that stubbornly refuses to part, in spite of all your praying and believing? *Check your obedience.* Is it up-to-date? As far as you know, have you done all God has instructed you to do? Or are you waiting for the waters to part first before you put your foot to the edge?

This principle of cooperating and corresponding works is found in Jesus' healing of the ten men with leprosy recorded in Luke 17. The lepers, seeing Jesus enter their village, cried out, 'Jesus, Master, have mercy on us!' (v. 13). Luke tells us that when Jesus saw them, 'He said to them, "Go and show yourselves to the priests." ' That was significant. When such a man was healed the law required that he be 'certified'—cured by the priests, before he was allowed once again to take his place as a normal citizen.

But these men with leprosy were not healed; they were still afflicted with that loathsome disease when Jesus commanded them to go to the priests. How could they act as though they were healed when they weren't? It isn't hard to imagine the thoughts that might have raced through their minds—the priests would rebuke them, the people would mock them. They would be the laughingstock of the whole village. Being a leper was bad enough without that.

But the Bible says, 'And it came about that as they were going, they were cleansed' (Luke 17:14). When were they cleansed? *As they were going.* As they were obeying. They stepped toward the door and it opened; they placed their feet in the water and the river parted. Their faith was completed by their cooperating and corresponding work. Had they insisted on waiting until they were healed before going to the priests, they would have died with leprosy.

One week in February of 1971, I was preparing a sermon on 2 Timothy 2:4: 'No soldier in active service entangles himself in the affairs of everyday life, so that he may please the one who enlisted him as a soldier.' The Lord spoke to me about my own entanglement. I was in financial bondage and had been for as long as I could remember. If God had wanted to move me to another field of service it would have taken extradition papers to get me out of Texas.

I was still making monthly payments on things I had bought for Christmas in 1969. We lived on the crumbling brink of financial disaster. I tried to save money, but every time our savings account got up to three or four dollars we had to take it out for some emergency. From my own experience and from the marriage counselling I had done as a minister, I knew that most of the problems between husbands and wives could be traced back to money problems.

On edge, irritable, quick-tempered, I found it impossible to give myself wholly to being a husband or father or minister with the strain of indebtedness that constantly harassed me. If God could deliver me from this, it would be a miracle second only to creation.

Believing that God wanted to and was able to liberate me from this entanglement, I knelt in my study and claimed His deliverance and, to cement the decision, announced my commitment to my wife and to my secretary. I believed God and publicly confessed my faith.

Guess what happened? Nothing. Things didn't improve one bit, financially. But my mind was at rest; I knew God had spoken to my heart and I was simply waiting for His promise to be fulfilled. But as time dragged by, I began to wonder—and worry.

Then in May of 1972, God spoke to me through another verse: Luke 6:38, which says, 'Give, and it will be given to you; good measure, pressed down, shaken together, running over, they will pour into your lap. For whatever measure you deal out to others, it will be dealt to you in return.' The verse wasn't new to me. I had read it many times, even preached on it. I believed it; it was in the Bible so I had to. But it had never come alive to my heart, had never been made real to me as it was that day. I knew that *that* was how God intended to deliver me from financial bondage. Here was a work that cooperated and corresponded to my faith.

Now, concerning that verse: I couldn't escape its meaning. I had been saying that when I got straightened out financially I was going to be more liberal in my giving. As a matter of fact, that was one of the reasons I was anxious to get out of debt–I wanted to be able to give freely and generously to the cause of Christ and to the needs of others. But I was practically eligible for foreign aid myself. So I told myself that when I got it I would give it. And then I met up with this verse. Instead of saying, 'When you get it, give it,' it had the audacity to say, *'When you give it, you will get it.'*

I said, 'Lord, I can't afford to give.'

He said, 'You can't afford not to.'

But what if my interpretation of that verse was wrong? I had never been as fastidious about correct interpretation as I was at that moment. Someone once asked me why I use so many illustrations involving money, and I replied that if people can learn to trust God in matters of finance, they can learn to trust Him about anything. In the battle of faith, money is usually the last stronghold to fall.

I decided to give it a try. I was willing to obey the light I had and trust God either to confirm or refute my interpretation of Luke 6:38. A few days later I was asked to conduct the funeral of a woman who was not a member of our church. Afterward a member of the family handed me an envelope containing a fifty dollar bill. It was the first time in my ministry I had ever been paid for conducting a funeral. I stuck the bill in my pocket.

That night after our midweek prayer service, as I walked from the worship centre to my office, I ran into a missionary on furlough who had visited our service that evening. As I talked with him, the Lord seemed to say, 'Give him the fifty dollars in your back pocket.' I excused myself and hurried into my office, wondering where in the world that voice had come from and how it knew exactly where I was keeping that fifty dollar bill. 'That could be the devil,' I said.

I thought about it a while, then said, 'Lord, if this is really You speaking–if you really want me to give this fifty dollars to that missionary, let me know beyond any doubt.' When it comes to parting with fifty dollars, you can't be too careful.

A few minutes later I left my office. If the missionary was gone (and he should have been since it was so late), I would have known that it had not been the Lord speaking to me. But when I walked outside, there he was, standing right where I had left him thirty minutes before. He was standing there by himself, as though he were waiting for someone–or something. I fished the fifty from my back pocket, gave it a last loving look, went over to the missionary, and pressed it into his hand. 'The Lord told me to give this to you,' I said.

And that was the beginning of my exodus from the land of bondage. By October of that year I was out of debt. Since then I have been able to meet every financial obligation on time, with enough left over to give generously to every good cause God has laid on my heart. God did not give me a thousand barrels of oil to salt away in a bank vault; He gave me one barrel of oil that never runs dry. I believe the best description of financial freedom is found in 2 Corinthians 9:8: 'And God is able to make all grace abound to you, that always having all sufficiency in everything, you may have an abundance for every good deed.'

God's promise to me was threefold: (1) every need adequately supplied; (2) every financial obligation met on time; (3) able to give generously to every good cause. But the promise did not become a possession until my works corresponded and cooperated with my faith.

For Instance...

Few verses are as precious to believers as Romans 8:28: 'And we know that God causes all things to work together for good to those who love God, to those who are called according to His purpose.' That's a fantastic promise. Just think of it—God takes everything that comes our way, good and bad, and by His sovereign power works it all together for our good and His glory. Whatever happens, God is going to see to it that it works out for our good. Ask the average Christian if he believes that verse and he will answer with a hearty 'Amen!'

Do you believe that verse? I do. Then why do we

grumble and gripe so much? Why do we hit the panic button when something unexpected happens that foils our well-laid plans? That is hardly a corresponding reaction. The corresponding work that cooperates with our faith is to stop complaining and 'in everything give thanks; for this is God's will for you in Christ Jesus' (1 Thessalonians 5:18).

A New Golden Rule

Consider the prayer promise in Matthew 7:11. Jesus said, 'If you then, being evil, know how to give good gifts to your children, how much more shall your Father who is in heaven give what is good to those who ask Him!' What is the act that corresponds to faith in this case? Prayer, of course, is the obvious answer. But, I think, the incorrect one.

Let's look at the following verse. It begins with the word 'therefore', which means Jesus is about to make a practical application of a truth just stated. 'Therefore whatever you want others to do for you, do so for them....' We call this the Golden Rule; but I'm afraid many people read it the wrong way. Like this: 'Therefore whatever you *don't* want others to do to you, *don't* do to them.'

In other words, if I don't want someone to punch me in the nose, I ought not to punch anybody else in the nose. And if I haven't done anything to anyone today that I wouldn't want done to me, I think I have obeyed the Golden Rule. But that is not what Jesus said or meant. The Golden Rule is positive, not negative. We are to take the initiative and *do* for others what we would want done for us.

Now see the connection between verse 11 and verse 12. In prayer we are asking God to do good things for us. All right; if we want God to do good things for us we must do good things for others. In short, we must treat others the way we want God to treat us. You see, the Golden Rule is actually this: *Do unto others as you would have God do unto you.*

Prayer is an act of faith, and the corresponding work that cooperates with that faith is doing good to others. If I want God to give me good things I must give good things to others. And if I really believe that God is going to give me good things, I can easily afford to give good things to others. I am convinced that many unanswered prayers can be traced back to our failure to obey this command.

Wisdom–Ours For The Asking

James 1:5 is a promise that has meant much to me in recent years. The apostle says, 'But if any of you lacks wisdom, let him ask of God, who gives to all men generously and without reproach, and it will be given to him.' This promise is made within the context of trials in the believer's life. James tells us that if we do not know what to do during a time of testing, we can ask God for wisdom and He will provide all that we need.

For years I approached that promise like this: In the midst of a trying situation I would ask God for

wisdom, claiming this particular promise. Then I
would wait for God to pump some wisdom into my
brain. I would wait and wait but rarely feel any
wiser. I saw no fiery writing in the sky instructing me
what to do; there was no sudden surge of divine
insight gushing into my mind. Then I would pray
again, hoping that this time my aim would be good
enough to hit the bullseye. Still no wisdom; still no
flutter of wings as angels bent low to whisper the
secret wisdom of heaven in my ear.

Then came a period when my wife and I lived in a
constant whirlwind of trials, with every day demanding wise and critical decisions. I felt anything but
wise; I was overwhelmed by the relentless pressure
created by the situation. Desperation drove me
again to this verse, and God in His goodness opened
my eyes to its truth. Studying the verse afresh, I
zeroed in on the last phrase: 'and it will be given
him.' Full stop. Just like that.

In the following verse James says that we are to
ask in faith 'without any doubting.' *Doubting* translates a Greek word that means to be at odds with
oneself, wavering between two opinions, separating
one from the other. It expresses a hesitation to act
affirmatively—a perfect description of what I had
been doing. Even as I prayed, I kept separating
things I thought possible from the things I thought
impossible.

After praying I was hesitant to act, unsure of
myself, uncertain if God had heard me. Categorizing
things as possible or impossible is rank unbelief, for

with God there is only one category: possible. My hesitation to act after asking God for wisdom was unbelief that voided my prayer.

I concluded that, to receive the answer, I must act on the assumption that God had given me the asked-for wisdom. He had promised to give it and I had the right to assume that *what seemed to be the wise decision was the right decision*, the decision that God Himself would make. In exercising my wisdom, I was exercising His wisdom. And so I did that which cooperated with and corresponded to my prayer of faith.

I made the decision as best I knew how, believing God was imparting to me His wisdom and insight. How could I claim God was giving me wisdom if I was afraid to make a decision? And I am happy to report that time has proven that every decision I made during those critical days was the correct one.

I cannot emphasize too strongly the importance of this principle. For every affirmation of faith there is a cooperating and corresponding act of obedience. The goal of faith is to get us out of the foyer and into every room of God's abundance. But that goal can be achieved only as we bring our obedience up-to-date by acting upon the Word of God.

CHAPTER ELEVEN

Waiting for the Promise

'Bible promises,' said Spurgeon, 'are like cheques drawn on heaven's bank that we endorse by faith and present to God for payment.'

True. But sometimes the cheques are post-dated! One of the most disturbing discoveries we make in the life of faith is that God does not operate according to our time schedule. We assume God will respond immediately to our prayers, and we rise from our knees expecting to find the answer standing before us. But more often than not, there is a waiting period between the asking and the receiving. And to twentieth-century Christians, this is a big problem.

In these days of instant coffee and instant credit, we have a low tolerance for delay. We demand everything right now, if not sooner. Eric Hoffer writes:

> If one were to pick the chief trait which characterizes the temper of our time it would be impatience. Tomorrow has become a dirty word.[1]

The interim between asking and receiving is a precarious time for the believer. His faith, growing more frustrated and fragile with each unfulfilled day, becomes vulnerable to the attacks of the enemy. Satan, ever the opportunist, would have us think that God's delay is God's denial; he whispers in our ear, 'Hath God said?' Our faith droops, our feelings sell out to the enemy, and doubt unpacks its suitcase for an extended visit.

Let's face it: if we are going to know the life of faith we must learn how to handle what J. Sidlow Baxter calls 'those strange delays.'[2]

Better Late Than Ever

The delays are as much a part of God's purpose as are the fulfilments. In fact, *the delays will usually prove a greater blessing than the fulfilments*. The full story as to why God delays His answers is buried in the mystery of His infinite wisdom; but here are some clues.

1. Sometimes God waits until we are spiritually mature enough to handle the blessing we are seeking. Every parent knows that he must determine not only what is good for his child, but also *when* it is good for him. The right thing given at the wrong time can be a curse rather than a blessing.

2. God may test the sincerity of our desire by withholding the object of our request. He is a rewarder of those who diligently seek Him (Hebrews 11:6).

3. God uses delay to strengthen our character. Remember that the 'testing of your faith produces endurance. And let endurance have its perfect

result, that you may be perfect and complete, lacking in nothing' (James 1:3, 4). God may use delay to draw us into a deeper communion with Him, the delay causing us to seek Him more earnestly.

4. Sometimes God withholds the blessing until the blessing becomes of secondary importance. It is dangerously easy to fix our heart on the blessing rather than the Blesser, on the gift instead of the Giver. Only when the Blesser overshadows the blessing are we truly ready to receive it. Hebrews 11:6 tells us that God is a rewarder of those who seek *Him*, not the reward. To repeat the words of Charles Wesley,

> Thy gifts alone cannot suffice,
> Except Thyself be given,
> For Thy presence makes my paradise,
> And where Thou art is heaven.

There is an intriguing statement concerning Abraham's faith in Hebrews 11. The writer says, 'By faith he lived as an alien in the land of promise, as in a foreign land, dwelling in tents with Isaac and Jacob, fellow-heirs of the same promise; for he was looking for the city which has foundations, whose architect and builder is God' (Hebrews 11:9, 10). And then the writer sums up the faith of Abraham and the others with these words: 'But as it is, they desire a better country, that is a heavenly one' (Hebrews 11:16).

Abraham lived *as an alien in the land of promise...looking for the city whose builder was God*. God promised to lead Abraham to a land of his own, and He did. Yet when Abraham arrived in that land, when at last he received the fulfilment of God's promise, he was not satisfied. Although he was in the land of promise, he looked beyond that land to the literal presence of God. To Abraham there was something more to be desired than the promise of God–the presence of God. Perhaps when he began the journey the land meant everything; but by the time he had reached his destination, God had become everything.

God's blessings are not an end in themselves. They are the means God uses to draw us to Himself. 'The goodness of God leadeth thee to repentance.' God may have to withhold the blessing until we come to love Him for Himself instead of what He can do for us; or, as someone put it, until we seek His face instead of His hand. God honours the faith that desires His fellowship more than His favours.

With God, *timing* is more important than time, and whatever the reason for the delay, we may rest assured that His timing is always perfect and that the delay is a vital part of His redemptive purpose. Let us learn to pray with George Matheson: 'My Father, help me to learn that I am heir to possessions which exceed my present holding! They exceed my present *power* to hold–they are waiting for my summer. Do I ever thank Thee for the blessings which Thou postponest? I am afraid not. I am like the prodigal: I want to get *all at once* the portion that falleth to me; and, where it is not given, I deem it is refused. Teach me, O Lord, the beauty of Thy delayed answers.'[3]

Hanging-on Faith

Faith can be seen as existing on two levels: faith as an initial act; and faith as a continuing activity or attitude. There is the faith that brings us to Jesus with our need; and there is the faith that keeps us there when the need is not immediately supplied. C.S. Lewis said, 'Faith is the art of holding on to things your reason once accepted, in spite of changing moods.'[4]

Of the various dimensions of faith, this is the most vital; and it is this kind of faith, more than any other, that we will be called upon to exercise. When everything we once easily believed seems suddenly improbable and illogical, it is 'hanging-on' faith that holds us on course and keeps our eyes fixed on the unfailing promises of God.

Jesus says to us, as He said to Jairus, 'Now don't be afraid, go on believing' (Luke 8:50, Phillips). Having presented the promise to God and having claimed it as ours, we must 'strike the pose of faith' and hold it until, in God's time, the promise is fulfilled.

Easier said than done. How do I strike this pose of faith and hold it against the onslaught of doubt and discouragement? Hebrews 10 contains a powerful example of 'hanging-on' faith. From the passage that follows we can learn the secret of waiting.

But remember the former days, when, after being enlightened, you endured a great conflict of sufferings, partly, by being made a public spectacle through reproaches and tribulations, and partly by becoming sharers with those who were so treated. For you showed sympathy to the prisoners, and accepted joyfully the seizure of your property, knowing that you have for yourselves a better possession and an abiding one. Therefore, do not throw away your confidence, which has a great reward. For you have need of endurance, so that when you have done the will of God, you may receive what was promised.

> FOR YET IN A VERY LITTLE WHILE,
> HE WHO IS COMING WILL COME, AND WILL
> NOT DELAY.
> BUT MY RIGHTEOUS ONE SHALL LIVE BY
> FAITH:
> AND IF HE SHRINKS BACK, MY SOUL HAS NO
> PLEASURE IN HIM.

But we are not of those who shrink back to destruction, but of those who have faith to the preserving of the soul (Hebrews 10:32-39).

The Christians to whom the author wrote were facing persecution so severe that their faith was threatened with collapse. There was even talk of defecting. To shore up the walls of their sagging faith and to enable them to emerge victorious from this trial, he reminded them of their previous trials and how they overcame them. He speaks of a 'great reward' (v. 35) and of receiving 'what was promised' (v. 36). The whole passage dovetails into that last phrase in verse 36–that is the end toward which everything moves: that 'you may receive what was promised.' Quite simply, the writer is telling them what they must do to receive what was promised.

This hanging-on faith that knows how to wait for the promise revolves around three key words: *confidence, obedience,* and *endurance.*

Waiting For The Promise Requires Confidence Based On God's Past Faithfulness

In verse 35 the author says, 'Therefore, do not throw away your confidence, which has a great reward.' Confidence, often translated 'boldness', is one of the great words of the New Testament and is a chief characteristic of believers. It means conspicuous courage in the face of adversity. It is the ability to face trials with a courageous calmness, to respond with Christlike meekness when wronged.

It is Job saying, 'Though He slay me yet will I serve Him.' It is Paul and Silas in prison with bleeding backs, yet singing praises at midnight. It is Peter and the apostles, when threatened by the religious leaders, saying, 'We must obey God rather than men.' It is Jesus, being reviled, refusing to revile in return, who, as Peter says, 'While suffering...uttered no threats, but kept entrusting Himself to Him who judges righteously' (1 Peter 2:23).

The word 'therefore' points back to the preceding

verses, which show that the believers' confidence came as a result of earlier experience. These Christians were not strangers to persecution, having encountered it soon after their conversion. It was then that they discovered the sufficiency of God's grace, and this gave birth to confidence in His faithfulness. Their confidence had sustained them in their previous sufferings and would see them through this one. Therefore, says the writer, don't cast it away; you are going to need it again.

Their confidence enabled them not only to endure shame and affliction, but to accept joyfully the seizure of their property. The key word is *joyfully*. A persecuted Christian may have no choice but to accept the loss of his possessions; but to accept it *joyfully* is another matter. They were able to do this 'knowing that you have for yourselves a better possession and an abiding one.' The experience taught them that, though the enemy might strip them of every earthly possession, their greatest possession, their wealth in Christ, could never be touched. Possessing nothing, they possessed everything. Loss of all worldly goods failed to diminish their assets. Bankrupt but rich, they were wealthy paupers.

And now it was happening again. As the angry waves of renewed persecution swept over them, the writer cried, 'Remember! Remember the former days. Don't throw away your confidence. Remember!'

The exhortation to remember is one of the most frequent in the Bible. It is the watchword of faith.

The past with its record of God's faithfulness is the Christian's greatest defence against encroaching discouragement. We preserve our confidence by remembering.

'I shall remember the deeds of the Lord; surely I will remember Thy wonders of old. I will meditate on all Thy work, and muse on Thy deeds' (Psalm 77:11, 12). Again and again, Israel, when cornered by catastrophe, believed its way to victory by recounting God's past mercies. Before he died, Moses rehearsed with the people all that God had done for the people and admonished them to remember.

Concerning the Lord's Supper, Christ said, 'Do this in remembrance of Me' (1 Corinthians 11:24). Is it possible that we could forget that Jesus died for us? Evidently, it is. We may remember the fact of it but forget the force of it. We quickly forget the goodness of God. Unbelief has a short memory.

I recall more than one occasion when, having been delivered by God's grace at the eleventh hour, I declared, 'I'll never doubt God again!' But in a few weeks—or days—when another seemingly impossible situation loomed on the horizon, I found myself cowering in the corner of self-pity, whimpering because God had abandoned me. Forgetfulness is definitely hazardous to your faith.

A Book Of Remembrances

Don't trust your memory. There's something about fallen human nature that finds it easy to forget spiritual things. We can remember a dirty joke we heard twenty years ago, but can't recall the preacher's text from last Sunday's sermon.

In 1970 I began keeping a record of answered prayers. For several years I faithfully jotted down in a little black book every specific answer, every instance of God's obvious mercy in times of trouble. Then I misplaced it and didn't recover it until two or three years later. I had moved my study from the church office to my home, and while unpacking a carton of books, I found it. How it got in the bottom of that box I'll never know—but there it was.

As I thumbed through it I was surprised to realize that I had forgotten most of the incidents mentioned. It was an opportune discovery, because at that time I was passing through a very trying period. To be honest, my faith was at an all-time low. But as I read through that little black book, something happened. My memory of God's wonderful faithfulness was revived and my sagging faith began to recover. By the time I read the last entry I was filled with rejoicing and *confidence*. Remembering had restored my confidence in the Lord.

There may come a time when you need to give your dying faith mouth-to-mouth resuscitation—and remembering is the best way to do it. Let me encourage you to start a Book of Remembrances. My Hebrew professor used to say, 'Paper is cheaper than brains.' You can find a good hardcover book filled with blank pages at most bookstores; or, if you prefer, a regular spiral notebook will do the trick. The important thing is to preserve a record of God's activity in your life. A chronicle of God's dealings and deliverances may someday mean the difference between victory and defeat.

> His love in time past
> Forbids me to think
> He'll leave me at last
> In trouble to sink;
> Each sweet Ebenezar
> I have in review,
> Confirms His good pleasure
> To help me quite through.
> *John Newton*

Waiting For The Promise Involves Obedience To God's Present Will

'For you have need of endurance, so that when you have done the will of God, you may receive what was promised' (Hebrews 10:36).

Faith is not idle; it works while it waits. Receiving what God has promised requires obedience. We cannot expect God to fulfil His promise if we do not fulfil His will.

In the chapter, 'How to Complete Your Faith', we discussed obedience as a part of faith–a distinctive act of obedience called for by a specific act of faith. Here the emphasis is upon continuing obedience to daily duty while we wait for God to respond to our faith.

It is significant that the writer, having exhorted his readers to cling to their confidence, makes no such appeal concerning obedience. If obedience is so important, why does he not here command them to obey? It is unnecessary.

Their obedience is assumed. Once confidence in the Lord has been established and firmly grounded, obedience will take care of itself. Obedience follows confidence as surely as thunder follows lightning. Even though it was obedience to God's will that got these people into trouble in the first place, God's past faithfulness had so clothed them with courageous confidence that they continued to obey regardless of the consequences. Only when confidence wavers does obedience hesitate.

When The Upright Get Uptight

The Psalmist said, 'Trust in the Lord, and do good' (Psalm 37:3). Here again confidence and obedience are linked together. This Psalm opens with a command to do the impossible: *'Fret not.'* He is telling the upright not to get uptight. But there's so much to fret about! And it's so easy; it takes hardly any effort at all. But as usual, the Bible tells us how to do the impossible.

The alternative to fretfulness is given in verse 3: 'Trust in the Lord, and do good.' If we aren't careful we will see only the first familiar words, 'Trust in the Lord,' and barely notice the others: 'and do good.' Having committed the fretful situation to the Lord, trusting Him to handle it, we are to turn our attention to our everyday duty–doing good.

Doing good is proof we are trusting the Lord. If the trial through which we are passing so unsettles us as to prevent us from carrying on in everyday obedience, we have not truly trusted the matter to God. In a word, we have cast away our confidence.

Satan's strategy is to distract us from the will of God by paralyzing us with fear and anxiety. As a pastor I have seen believers incapacitated by worry to the extent that they could not function even in the simple details of daily living. But we have all felt that numbing preoccupation with a problem that drains the heart of all courage and concern; that awful lethargy that creeps over us because we have lost heart. The only effective counterattack is to trust the Lord. Trusting God to handle these fretful circumstances frees us to do His will without distraction. We overcome the evil by doing good.

I believe this is the point Christ makes in Matthew 6. He tells us not to be anxious for our life, what we shall eat or drink or wear, because our heavenly Father will see to it that we have all these things. Then comes the climax of the passage: 'But seek first His kingdom and His righteousness; and all these things shall be added to you' (Matthew 6:33).

In other words, our concern is not to be with the physical and the material, but with the spiritual, with the kingdom of God and His righteousness. The point is, a person cannot seek *first* the things of God if his mind is preoccupied with the things of this world. It is the care of the world and the deceitfulness of riches (the mistaken belief that riches can erase the care of the world) that prevent the Word of God from bearing fruit in our hearts (Matthew 13:22).

Why does God promise to supply all our needs (Philippians 4:19)? Is it merely that we may have all we need? No, I think there is more to it than that. After all, even unbelievers have their needs supplied. Matter of fact, I know some unbelievers whose supply wagons carry much bigger loads than mine. Remember, while God is concerned about our physical life, His primary concern is with the spiritual. I believe the chief reason God promises to provide for our physical needs is so we can be free to seek Him and His kingdom. It works like this: If I don't have to worry about my life-needs, I can give my whole heart to seeking and serving Him.

Not long after graduating from seminary I was called to pastor a church in East Dallas. The former pastor had retired and remained a member of the church. In fact, it was he who recommended my name to the pulpit committee. A gracious and wise man, he later became a close friend and confidant. But when I was moving into the pastor's study he paid me a visit. He quietly told me that on his last Sunday as pastor of the church he had asked the church to take a certain action that would affect me.

'I hope you won't mind what I did,' he said.

'What did you do?'

'I asked the church to increase your salary by seventy-five dollars a week.'

'No,' I said. 'I don't mind. I don't mind at all. Not at all.'

And then he said, 'Now I didn't do that for you. I did it for this church.'

'I don't think I understand,' I said.

'Son,' he said, 'you can't do your best for the Lord or this church if you're having to worry about making ends meet. I want you to be free to give your best.'

That was a wise man. And that is exactly what Jesus is saying in Matthew 6. God wants us free to concentrate all our heart-attention on His will and righteousness. And trusting our physical and material needs to God gives us that freedom.

Our confidence in God expresses itself by obedience. While we wait for the promise, we must keep our obedience up-to-date.

Waiting For The Promise Demands Patience For God's Future Work

'For you have need of endurance, so that when you have done the will of God, you may receive what was promised' (Hebrews 10:36). The third condition for receiving the promise is endurance, or *patience*, as the word is often translated. Patience is the bridge between the doing of God's will and the receiving of the promise. Receiving what God has promised hinges not only upon doing God's will but on enduring after that will has been done. Many fail to receive because they fail to endure.

The writer is using the language of the athlete. A football team may be leading its opponents by one goal, but if the players leave the field before the final whistle they will lose the game. The same is true with faith. We may be filled with courageous confidence, we may obey all God's will; but if we lack patience, we will lose the reward.

This patience, which Philo calls the 'queen of virtues', is more than mere waiting or passive resignation. Barclay observes that 'there is no single English word which transmits all the fullness of its meaning.'[5] The Greek word literally means, 'an abiding under,' and contains the ideas of steadfastness, constancy, staying power. Another writer describes it as 'a lively outgoing power of faith, and active energy.'[6]

Ellicott says:

> In this noble word there always appears a background of courage. It does not mark merely the endurance, but also the perseverance, the brave patience with which the Christian contends against the various hindrances, persecutions, and temptations that befall him in his conflict with the inward and outward world.[7]

This word is used most often in connection with trials. In classical Greek it was used of a plant's ability to live under hard and unfavourable circumstances.[8] If, as the writer to the Hebrews says, we *need* endurance, then we can expect to encounter difficulty. Mark it well: *faith never escapes testing*.

Is This Trial Necessary?

Somewhere along the way we picked up the idea that if a person commits his life to Christ and sincerely trusts the Lord, he will sail through life on calm seas. But both the Bible and our own experience testify that this is not the case. The apostle Peter wrote to early believers, 'In this you greatly rejoice, even though now for a little while, *if necessary*, you have been distressed by various trials, that the proof of your faith, being more precious than gold which is perishable, even though tested by fire, may be found to result in praise and glory and honour at the revelation of Jesus Christ' (1 Peter 1:6, 7, emphasis mine).

Faith must be tested. An untried faith is an untrustworthy faith, because until it is put to the test we can never be sure if what we are calling faith is really faith. If there is a defect in our faith we need to know. That's why they test aeroplanes before they are mass-produced. And that's why test pilots are paid so well.

Not long ago, on our way to California, my family and I spent the night in Albuquerque, New Mexico. The next morning as I was loading our luggage into the boot, a car came creeping through the car park and stopped beside me. A man and woman were inside and the man had a road map spread open over the steering wheel. He smiled and said hello and asked if I could help him. Assuming he was lost and wanted to ask directions, I went over to the car and told him I would be glad to if I could.

Suddenly he pulled his hand from under the road map and held up for my inspection a beautiful gold necklace.

'Like to buy a solid gold necklace cheap?' he said.

I glanced nervously over my shoulder, expecting to see police cars bearing down on us with lights flashing and sirens screaming. 'Uh, no, thank you,' I said, backing away. Why was I *thanking* him?

The necklace vanished and he jerked open his sports coat. 'How about a genuine Rolex watch?' Pinned to the inside of his jacket was a wristwatch.

'No, thanks,' I said and hauled myself out of there.

Back in the room, I told my wife what had happened, knowing she would share my indignation which she did, of course.

At first. Then, wistfully, she said, 'You know, I'll bet we could have bought that necklace for next to nothing.'

My wife is a great joker.

But a person would be a fool to buy a necklace under those conditions. In the first place, it was probably so hot it smoked. And in the second place, all that glitters is not gold. The necklace could have been electroplated or only gold-plated. It would be stupid to buy it without having it tested.

All that glitters is not gold, and all that belief is

not faith. And it is only by testing that we can determine the authenticity of our faith.

Also, it is by testing our faith that Christian
character is produced (James 1:3, 4). And isn't that
the real goal of our Christian experience—not that
we might 'get the blessing' but that our character be
perfected? James tells us to count it all joy when we
fall into various trials (James 1:2); but we can do that
only if character means more to us than comfort.

Resignation vs. Anticipation

But there is another, perhaps more important,
quality found in biblical patience: *expectation.* Biblical patience is not waiting with resignation but waiting with anticipation; it is waiting for something or
someone. The word is often connected with some
great and glorious goal. Barclay sums it up well:

> It is not the patience which can sit down and
> bow its head and let things descend upon it and
> passively endure until the storm is past.... It is
> the spirit which can bear things, not simply with
> resignation, but with blazing hope; it is not the
> spirit which sits statically enduring in one place,
> but the spirit which bears things because it
> knows that these things are leading to a goal of
> glory; it is not patience which grimly waits for
> the end, but the patience which radiantly hopes
> for the dawn.[9]

The Psalmist tells us that waiting for the Lord is like waiting for the sunrise (Psalm 130:6). In waiting for the sunrise you can always count on two things: one, you can't rush it. Nothing you can do will hurry it; setting your clock ahead won't cause it to rise ahead of schedule. You must wait for it to rise in its own time. Two, the sun *does* rise. It always has and it always will. Those who wait for the morning are never disappointed. Neither are those who wait for the Lord.

Patient endurance—it even *sounds* awful; it sounds grim and cheerless and foreboding. Few things in life are more unappealing, more agonizing, more maddening, than waiting. How is it possible to stand calmly on the deck of a storm-battered ship and wait patiently for God to still the tempest?

It is the element of *anticipation* that makes such patient endurance possible. And that is what the author of Hebrews is speaking of in verse 37:

FOR YET IN A VERY LITTLE WHILE, HE WHO IS COMING WILL COME, AND WILL NOT DELAY.

This is a quotation from Habakkuk 2:3. There the people were waiting for God to destroy the Chaldeans who were laying siege to the city and threatening them with destruction. The prophecy opens with Habakkuk's complaint that his repeated cries to the Lord for help have gone unanswered. Now in the second chapter God speaks in answer to the prophet's complaint. The purpose and promise of

God will be fulfilled, the Lord says. Even though it appears to linger, it will be fulfilled in its due time.

The writer of Hebrews takes up the theme and applies it to the present situation. 'He who is coming will come, and will not delay.' It may look like delay to those waiting, but the Lord is right on schedule.

The phrase, 'He who is coming,' is literally, 'the Coming One,' the participle indicating character; that is His constant attitude, not an occasional activity. In other words, His coming is more than a response to their prayers; it is a response to His character. Not to come in deliverance and promise would be to deny His own nature. He is always coming; He is ever the Coming One. We could say, He is always *in transit*.

It's In The Air

In 1975 I resigned the pastorate to enter a full-time travelling ministry. Knowing ahead of time that I would do this, the Lord caused the country's largest airport, the Dallas/Ft. Worth Regional Airport, to be built within two miles of my house just so it would be convenient for my wife, Kaye, to meet my late-night flights (not many people are aware of this).

A few years ago I was flying home from a conference up north, scheduled to arrive on Flight 214 at midnight. Kaye arrived a few minutes before twelve and went to the gate to meet me. Twelve o'clock came but the plane didn't. Nothing unusual about that, so she waited. But after a while she went to the ticket counter and asked the agent when they expected Flight 214.

In about thirty minutes,' the agent said.

Kaye decided to wait in the car and listen to the radio. Thirty minutes later she returned to the gate but the flight still hadn't arrived. She went back to the ticket counter. 'Any word on Flight 214?'

'Looks like another thirty minutes, at least.'

Another thirty minutes dragged by. With the exception of the few people waiting to meet Flight 214, the terminal was practically deserted.

'It's me again. Look, don't you know when 214's going to be here?'

The agent looked up from the stack of papers he was sorting. 'I'm sorry, but we do not have that information. Check back later.'

Puzzled, my wife wandered around the terminal waiting for a decent interval to pass when she could go back to the ticket counter.

'Excuse me,' she said, 'but you must have some idea when the plane is going to be here.'

Again the agent stopped what he was doing and looked at her without smiling. 'I'm sorry, ma'am, but we do not have that information.'

'Well,' she insisted, 'at least you can tell me what time it left!'

'I'm sorry, but we do not have that information. If you would check back in a few minutes....'

She couldn't understand the agent's strange behaviour and why it had changed so suddenly. Surely they knew what time a flight took off; no big

mystery about that. Why not tell her? Unless....
And then it hit her. She rushed back to the ticket
counter, with visions of crashed and burning planes
in her head.

'Listen!' she said to the agent. 'About Flight 214! I
don't want to know when it left. I don't want to
know when it's going to get here. But can you tell me
just one thing? *Is it in the air?*'

The agent smiled and said, 'Yes, it's in the air.'

'Thank you. That's all I need to know.'

And the rest of the waiting was easy. She could
wait with patience, knowing it was in the air.

And there have been times in my life, times of
unexplained trials and unrelieved heartaches, when I
have come to the Lord and asked, 'Lord, why?' and
the answer has been, 'I'm sorry, but I can't give you
that information.'

'Lord,' I have cried, 'how long? When will You
deliver me from all this?'

'I'm sorry, but I can't give you that information.'

And in desperation, I have cried, 'Lord, can You
telll me just this much: not when You will end this or
how You will end it. But just this: Is it in the air?'

And the Lord has said, 'Yes, child, it is in the air.'

And that has been enough. I can wait patiently for
the Lord because I know He *is* coming; He is always
coming. He is on the way. It is in the air.

> Thus far we prove that promise good,
> Which Jesus ratified with blood.

Still He is faithful, wise and just,
And still in Him believers trust.

Notes

1. Eric Hoffer, *The Temper of Our Time* (New York: Harper & Row, Publishers, 1967), p. 120.
2. J. Sidlow Baxter, *Does God Still Guide?* (Grand Rapids: Zondervan Publishing House, 1968), p. 155.
3. Edwin and Lillian Harvey, *Kneeling We Triumph* (Chicago: Moody Press, 1974), p. 31.
4. C. S. Lewis, *The Best of C. S. Lewis* (Grand Rapids: Baker Book House, 1969), p. 513.
5. William Barclay, *A New Testament Wordbook* (London: SCM Press, 1955), p. 59.
6. Alan Richardson, ed., *A Theological Wordbook of the Bible* (New York: The Macmillan Company, 1960), p. 165. Copyright © 1950, and renewed 1978, by Macmillan Publishing Co., Inc.
7. C. Leslie Mitton, *The Epistle of James* (Grand Rapids: Wm. B. Eerdmans Publishing Co., 1966), p. 23.
8. Barclay, p. 59.
9. *Ibid.*, p. 60.

CHAPTER TWELVE

A Final Word–
How Faith Grows

God allows us to set the level and the limit of our own blessings. In a very real sense, we determine the extent to which God uses or blesses us. When we pray, as we often do, 'Lord, bless me more,' I think I can hear the Lord reply, 'Child, I'm blessing you now all you will let me.'

Let's look at some Scripture passages:

'Give, and it will be given to you; good measure, pressed down, shaken together, running over, they will pour into your lap. *For whatever measure you deal out to others, it will be dealt to you in return*' (Luke 6:38, emphasis added).

'For in the way you judge, you will be judged; *and by your standard of measure, it shall be measured to you*' (Matthew 7:2, emphasis added).

'And He was saying to them, "Take care what you listen to. *By your standard of measure it shall be measured to you*; and more shall be given you besides." ' (Mark 4:24, emphasis added).

Matthew records the incident of two blind men following Jesus, begging Him to heal them: 'And after He had come into the house, the blind men came up to Him, and Jesus said to them, "Do you believe that I am able to do this?" They said to Him,

"Yes, Lord." Then He touched their eyes, saying, "*Be it done to you according to your faith*" ' (Matthew 9:28, 29, emphasis added).

An excellent illustration of this principle is found in 2 Kings 4, the story of the widow and the pot of oil. The woman's husband had died, leaving her two children and an unpaid debt, and the creditor planned to make slaves of her sons. When she turned to Elisha for help, the prophet asked what she had in her house. Evidently, he had in mind staging the first garage sale in history. Anyway, she told him she had nothing in the house except a pot of oil, hardly worth mentioning.

The prophet instructed her to gather all the empty vessels she could and fill them from the one jar of oil; then she could sell the oil, pay off the creditor, and save her sons. Without any hesitation, the woman obeyed the outlandish words of this strange prophet. And the miracle happened. But notice what occurred in verse 6: 'And it came about when the vessels were full, that she said to her son, "Bring me another vessel." And he said to her, "There is not one vessel more." *And the oil stopped*' (emphasis added).

The oil stopped. As long as there was room to receive it, the oil poured forth. The flow of the oil was determined, not by God's ability to give it, but by the woman's capacity to receive it. If, when the flow stopped, the woman had prayed, 'Lord, give me more oil,' I am certain the Lord would have said, 'Woman, give me more vessels!'

Many folks are praying for more oil when they ought to be gathering more vessels. If we are spiritually impoverished, it is not because the hand of grace is tight-fisted; it is because the hand of faith is too weak. The hand of faith is smaller than the hand of grace.

A few years ago a supermarket staged a contest in which the winner was allowed to plunge his hands into a barrel filled with silver dollars, keeping all his hands could hold. As the winner leered at the barrel of glittering silver dollars, he said, 'I wish I had bigger hands.'

F. B. Meyer said, 'If only a soul can believe in God, to the extent to which it believes it can obtain anything that is in the heart of God to bestow.'[1] If the law of the Christian life is 'according to your faith,' then it is vital that our faith grow.

Differing Degrees Of Faith

In chapter three I stated that with faith the main thing is the object of faith and not its size. But that is not to say that size is unimportant. Jesus rebuked little faith (Matthew 6:30; 8:26; 14:31; 16:8) and commended great faith (Matthew 8:10; 15:28).

That faith can and should grow is evidence from the use of such phrases as 'little faith' and 'great faith'. Paul looked forward to the increase of the Corinthians' faith (2 Corinthians 10:15). He longed to go to Thessalonica to complete what was lacking in the faith of the believers there (1 Thessalonians

3:10); and in his second letter to them he wrote of their faith enlarging (2 Thessalonians 1:3). In Romans 1:17, Paul employs the phrase, 'from faith to faith,' which Charles B. Williams translates, 'the way of faith that leads to greater faith.'

The book of Acts speaks of certain men as being 'full of faith' (Acts 6:5, 8; 11:24). This phrase seems to indicate a habitual characteristic as opposed to an occasional activity. What was an exception in some had become the rule in others. All Christians experience the periodic gift of faith during times of extremity. But there is a vast difference between these intermittent acts of faith, 'emergency rations', as it were, and the continuing, day-by-day posture of faith. It is the difference between scraping the bottom of the barrel for a crumb of faith and a constant resting in an abundant supply. To one, faith is a last resort; to the other it is the first response.

Paul describes Abraham as growing strong in faith (Romans 4:20). As we have seen, Abraham's faith is the standard for all believers. Using him as our example, we may say that strong faith is (1) *believing before the fact*; that is, believing when there is nothing to base our faith upon except the bare Word of God; and (2) *believing in spite of the facts*; that is, believing when outward circumstances contradict everything God has said.

John White defines great faith in this way: 'Great faith is responding to God when it is hardest to do so, either when the thing he demands of you hurts or else seems totally impractical... it is faith that continues to respond to the Word of God in the absence of outward encouragement.'[2]

We are strong or great in faith when the first and natural response to crisis or need is trust. It is trusting God by choice rather than by circumstance or force.

How Faith Grows

Basically God uses two cooperating methods to increase our faith: knowledge and experience.

1. Knowledge

Knowledge of God Himself. Remember the word of the Psalmist: 'And those who know thy name will put their trust in Thee' (Psalm 9:10). The name of God is God—as He has revealed Himself to us, His nature, His character, His purpose. Having discussed this in earlier chapters, suffice it to say that faith grows in much the same way it was born—as it looks unto Jesus.

Knowledge of God's Word. 'Faith comes from hearing, and hearing by the word of Christ' (Romans 10:17). Spurgeon said, 'The sight of the promises themselves is good for the eyes of faith: the more we study the words of grace, the more grace shall we derive from the words.'[3] The Word of God planted in the heart becomes a seed that will inevitably blossom, when watered with obedience, into a striking flower of faith. Your faith will grow in direct proportion to your knowledge of and commitment to the Word.

> How firm a foundation, ye saints of the Lord,
> Is laid for your faith in His excellent Word!
> What more can He say than to you He hath said,
> To you who for refuge to Jesus have fled?

Knowledge of God's works. By this, I mean the testimonies of others. It was the testimony of the Samaritan woman that drew all the men of her village out to see and hear Jesus. And remember, the witnesses of Hebrews 11 are not 'spectator witnesses' but 'testifying witnesses'. My own faith was greatly helped by reading the story of J. Hudson Taylor in *Hudson Taylor's Spiritual Secret.* Read the biographies of men and women who knew what it meant to trust God; they are nourishing food for a growing faith.

2. Experience

I have two statements to make:

Statement 1: We learn to trust God by trusting God.

We do not learn to trust God by listening to sermons on trusting God or by reading books on faith (even this one). We learn to trust by trusting. As we exercise what faith we have, it grows and develops into a stronger, healthier faith. It is by experience that we discover God can really be trusted after all, and that He does keep His promises.

When David was trying to persuade Saul to let him have a crack at Goliath, the lad was almost cocky in his belief that God would be with him. But he had good reason to be. God had already proved Himself faithful by enabling David to slay a lion and a bear that attacked the flock he had been tending. 'The Lord who delivered me from the paw of the lion and from the paw of the bear, He will deliver me from the hand of this Philistine' (1 Samuel 17:37).

> I thank God for the mountains
> And I thank Him for the valleys,
> I thank Him for the storms He brought me through,
> For if I'd never had a problem
> I wouldn't know that He could solve them,
> I'd never know what faith in God could do.[4]

We sometimes sing a little chorus that says, 'Jesus is all I need.' That's true, but we'll never know He is all we need until He is all we've got.

Statement 2: We will not trust God until we have to.

There is something about fallen human nature that finds it terribly difficult to 'lean not unto our own understanding' and to trust in the Lord. As long as we have one more trick up our sleeve, one more gimmick in our hand, one more dollar in the bank, we'll not trust God. I know there are exceptions, but that's exactly what they are—exceptions.

But if we only learn to trust by trusting, and if we

will not trust until we have to, then God must see to it that we have to.

The old saints used to have a phrase we would do well to revive: to be *shut up to faith*. Being shut up to faith meant being in a situation in which there was no choice but to trust God. The only way out was up. Having closed off every other avenue of escape, God had them shut up to faith. Other options were swept away. Like it or not, it was sink or swim, trust God or perish.

Israel at the Red Sea, for instance. That's a classic example of how God shuts us up to faith. With the mountains on either side and all the Egyptians in the world swooping down from behind, only *forward* was left. And forward was the Red Sea. And that's what God told them to do: Go forward—into the Red Sea. And they did. It was either trust God or be delivered again into bondage. But do you think they would have moved an inch in the direction of the Red Sea had not the Egyptians been behind them, encouraging them to do so? Not on your life.

Understanding this 'way of God' will unravel a lot of mysteries and explain a lot of pressure-cooker situations in which we have found ourselves. Often God is simply shutting us up to faith.

A number of years ago I read the biography of George Mueller, that great saint of Bristol, who for years supported a large orphanage by nothing but prayer and faith. The stories of his great faith set a fire in my heart. I longed to be able to trust God like that. I remember kneeling one day in my study and praying earnestly that God would teach me to live by faith. I guess I thought God would wave a wand over my head, and suddenly I would be a giant of faith, waiting for a vacancy in Hebrews 11. Instead, everything came unglued. Financial problems, ministerial difficulties, family crises–somebody was definitely out to get me. I went to my knees, begging God to help me, asking what was happening and why.

'I'm just answering your prayer,' He seemed to say.

'Prayer? What prayer? I don't remember praying for disaster.'

'Your prayer for faith,' He said.

Later I came across this piece by an unknown author.

THE LORD'S WAY

I asked the Lord that I might grow
In faith and love and every grace—
Might more of His salvation know,
And seek more earnestly His face.

'Twas He who taught me thus to pray,
And He, I trust, has answered prayer;
But it has been in such a way
As almost drove me to despair.

I hoped that in some favoured hour
At once He'd answer my request;
And, by His love's consuming power,
Subdue my sins, and give me rest.

Instead of this, He made me feel
The hidden evils of my heart,
And let the angry powers of hell
Assault my soul in every part.

Yes, more, with His own hand He seemed
Intent to aggravate my woe;
Crossed all the fair designs I schemed,
Blasted my guards, and laid them low.

'Lord, why is this?' I trembling cried:
'Wilt Thou pursue Thy worm to death?'
''Tis in this way,' the Lord replied,
'I answer prayer for grace and faith.

'These inward trials I employ,
From self and pride to set thee free
And break the schemes of earthly joy,
That thou mayest seek thy all in Me.'

God's greatest and toughest task is teaching us to trust Him, for without faith it is impossible to please Him. And He will do whatever is necessary to enroll us in that school from which there is no graduation.

Notes

1. F. B. Meyer, *Through Fire and Blood* (New York: Fleming H. Revell, 1896), p. 10.
2. John White, *The Fight* (Downers Grove: InterVarsity Press, 1976), pp. 102, 103.
3. C. H. Spurgeon, *Faith's Checkbook* (Chicago: Moody Press, n.d.), p. ii.
4. *Through It All*, Words and music by Andraé Crouch, published by Manna Music, Inc., Burbank, California, 1971.